Healthy Choices

Grades 4–5

A Positive Approach to Healthy Living

- Self-management
- Diet
- Exercise

Published by World Teachers Press®

www.worldteacherspress.com

Published with the permission of R.I.C. Publications Pty. Ltd.

First published by R.I.C. Publications Pty. Ltd., Perth, Western Australia. Revised by Didax Educational Resources.

Printed in the United States of America.

Order Number 2-5254
ISBN 978-1-58324-231-5

B C D E F 10 09 08 07 06

395 Main Street
Rowley, MA 01969
www.didax.com

HEALTHY CHOICES

Foreword

Living in a modern technological society can have detrimental effects on our health. On average, we are less active and consume far more fast food than is recommended by health experts. These kinds of habits are causing health problems like obesity and diabetes to develop much earlier in life than ever before. It is up to adults to guide and encourage children to live in a healthy way.

Healthy Choices, 4–5 aims to increase students' awareness of healthy lifestyles, helping them to develop positive habits that will stay with them into adulthood.

The book is divided into four sections:

- A Healthy Lifestyle
- A Healthy Diet
- Exercise and Fitness
- Self-Management

Other titles in this series are:

- *Healthy Choices, 1–3*
- *Healthy Choices, 6–8*

Contents

Healthy Choices is divided into four sections –

- *A Healthy Lifestyle* focuses on the benefits of a healthy lifestyle and the effects of unhealthy habits.

- *A Healthy Diet* focuses on the benefits of good nutrition and the problems with junk food.

- *Exercise and Fitness* focuses on the benefits of physical activity and how everyone can keep fit.

- *Self-Management* focuses on how we can make healthy choices for ourselves to increase our general well-being and self-esteem.

Teacher Page

A teacher page accompanies each student worksheet. It provides the following information:

The title shows the particular activity from the section being covered.

The subtitle shows which of the four sections of the book is being covered.

Specific indicators explain what the students are expected to demonstrate through completing the activities.

Teacher information has been provided to enhance the teacher's understanding of the concept being taught and to provide additional information to relate to the students. It also offers instructions for the activity.

Additional activities can be used to further develop the outcomes being assessed and clarify the concepts and skills taught in the activity. The additional activities may involve other curriculum areas.

Answers to all worksheet activities are given. Some answers may need a teacher check, while others will vary, depending on the students' personal experiences and opinions.

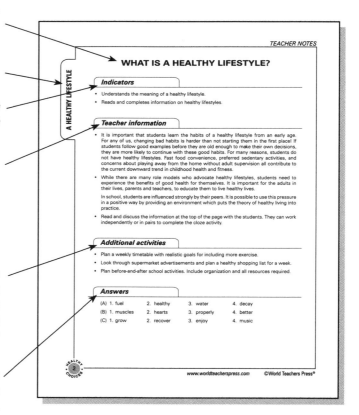

HEALTHY CHOICES

Student worksheet

The student activities reinforce and develop understanding of the concept and are largely language-based. A variety of student worksheets is provided, which may contain information to read, discussion topics and questions to answer.

The subtitle shows which of the four sections of the book is being covered.

The title shows the particular activity from the section being covered.

Most student pages begin with some **background information** which the student will need to complete the activities on the worksheet.

Questions to answer or activities to complete form the major part of the worksheet. All student instructions are concisely and clearly written to enable the students to work independently, if required.

The Health Challenge provides a practical application of the worksheet to be completed at home or independently by the student to link home and school.

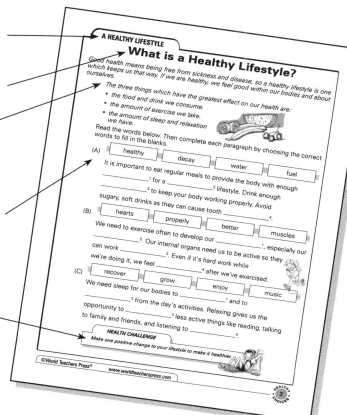

The final activity on each student worksheet—**Health Challenge**—is intended to extend learning about healthy lifestyles to the home environment. The emphasis in each Health Challenge is on the student to complete the activity, providing information to parents without being didactic or threatening in any way. These activities need not be corrected by the teacher, but may be used as a homework activity, if desired. It is hoped that through this activity, home and school may work together to develop a better awareness of health issues facing the adults of the future.

Healthy Choices aims to introduce and develop the knowledge, skills, attitudes and values that will enable students to lead healthy and fulfilling lives. Students will consider what it means to be healthy—physically, socially, mentally and emotionally—and will be given tools to help them become responsible for their own well-being.

Many of the activities in this book provide students with an opportunity to formulate their thoughts on a topic and express their opinions and feelings. Classroom discussions are invaluable resources for encouraging critical and reflective thinking.

NOTE: It is especially important for teachers, teaching assistants and other adults working with the students to be aware of sensitive factors such as poor home background, economic factors and individual weight problems, which could cause some students to feel uncomfortable when completing these worksheets.

Assessment Forms

The following explanation details how to use the **Assessment Form—Knowledge** on page vii.

Learning area
• Complete the appropriate learning area; for example: A healthy lifestyle.

Task(s)
• Give a brief description of the activity and what was expected of the students.

Outcome(s)
• Write the relevant outcome(s) which the activity satisfies (see outcome links below).

Assessment
• Write the relevant indicator(s) and assess appropriately.

Teacher comment
• Use this space to comment on aspects of an individual student's performance which cannot be indicated in the formal assessment, such as work habits or particular needs or abilities.

The following explanation details how to use the **Assessment Form—Skills and Attitudes** on page viii.

Assessment
• Assess the specific development of an individual student in these areas.

Teacher comment
• Use this space to comment on an individual student's skills and attitudes.

Student Forms

Although there are different types of diaries for food, exercise and sleep included in this book, the following additional forms have also been included on pages xiv – xix.

ASSESSMENT FORM
– KNOWLEDGE

Name

Date

Learning area

Task(s)

The student was asked to:

Outcome(s)

Assessment

The student:	*Demonstrated*	*Needs further opportunity*

Teacher comment

ASSESSMENT FORM
– SKILLS AND ATTITUDES

Name

Date

Assessment

The student:	Demonstrated	Needs further opportunity
• recognizes the importance to personal health of physical activities		
• recognizes the importance to personal health of a balanced diet		
• recognizes the importance to personal health of adequate relaxation and sleep		
• makes decisions for himself/herself		
• displays evidence of self-management skills		
• participates in and enjoys group activities		
• sets personal goals		
• achieves personal goals		
• communicates effectively		
• listens effectively		
• appreciates the similarities and differences between himself/herself and others		
• has a positive self-image		
• shows sensitivity towards others		
• recognizes the need for balance between diet, exercise, relaxation and sleep		

Teacher comment

HEALTHY CHOICES

Glossary of terms

A

active:	moving; carrying out actions; busy; lively
additive:	a substance added to a product to improve its quality or to preserve it
aerobic activity:	exercise in which the heartbeat increases above its normal rate for an extended period of time
allergen:	a substance which might produce an allergic reaction
anaerobic activity:	exercise done in quick, short bursts
artery:	a blood vessel which carries blood from the heart to other parts of the body

B

balance:	having objects in equal relation with each other; equilibrium; having equal importance
blood cholesterol:	a group of steroid alcohols derived from plants and animals found in the blood, usually indicated in a range from low to high and associated with the risk of heart disease
blood pressure:	the pressure of the blood against the inner walls of the blood vessels
blood sugar:	the quantity or percentage of glucose in the blood. Blood sugar concentration is a factor in diabetes.
body image:	the way a person perceives his/her body to be or appear
brain:	a greyish–and–whitish mass of nerve tissues which fill the skull of humans and other vertebrates; the center of sensation, body coordination, thought and emotion; a part of the nervous system

C

cancer	an abnormal growth or tumor which often reoccurs
calorie:	a unit of measurement for the quantity of heat output or energy from a food source
carbohydrates:	a group of foods or organic compounds which include simple sugars such as glucose and lactose, as well as polymers such as cellulose, starch and glycogen
carbon dioxide:	a colorless, odorless, incombustible gas (CO_2) present in the atmosphere and formed during the action of breathing
cardiovascular:	relating to the blood vessels and the heart
cholesterol:	a sterol (steroid alcohol derived from plants or animals) found in bile and gallstones, and in the brain and blood
circulation:	the recurring movement of the blood through the various vessels of the body
coordination:	the act of coordinating, the state of being able to place in harmonious relation or action

D

daily intake:	the amount of a substance, particularly food or drink, consumed each day
dehydration:	the state of being deprived of water; to lose water or moisture

Glossary of terms

D

depression: to suffer a state of feeling low in spirits, dejected, despondent, characterized by feelings of inadequacy, lowered activity, sadness and pessimism

diabetes: a disease in which the ability of the body to use sugar is impaired and sugar appears abnormally in the urine. Symptoms include an excessive need to urinate, excessive thirst, tiredness, blurred vision, recurrent skin infections and weight loss. Diabetes may take two forms— type 1 (insulin dependent diabetes), which is usually found in people under 40, and type 2 (non-insulin dependent diabetes), which is usually found in adults over 50. Type 1 is the more severe form. There is no known cure for diabetes. Treatment includes diet control and exercise, and tablets or insulin injections.

diet: the quantities and composition of food taken and its effect on health

digestion: the process by which food is taken into the systems of the body

disease: illness; sickness

E

eating disorder: a lack of order in eating habits; non-usual eating habits

endorphin: a natural pain-killing hormone

energy: the habit, ability or capacity of a person to carry out physical activity; exerting power; activity

excessive: exceeding the normal limit(s)

exercise: a bodily (or mental) exertion, usually as a means of training or improvement

F

fat: fleshy; obese; having a comparatively high oil content

fast food: food for sale, such as chicken, french fries and hamburgers, which can be made quickly

fiber: undigested food materials which can aid the removal of wastes from the body and provide bulk to the contents of the large intestine

fit: in good health or physical condition

fitness: the state of being fit

flexibility: the ability to bend

G

genetically-modified: having had the genetic origin changed

goal: something which is desired or to be attained requiring effort: an aim to an end

gymnastics: exercises requiring flexibility, strength and agility

H

healthy: having and enjoying good health

heart: the organ which pumps blood throughout the body

HEALTHY CHOICES

Glossary of terms

H

heart disease: any condition which adversely affects the actions of the heart

hobbies: a leisure-time activity or pursuit; an activity done for recreation

hormones: any of a group of various substances which are formed in cells in one part of an organism and transported to another part of the organism where they have an effect. Hormones may be of animal or plant origin.

J

joints: the movable places or parts where two bones or body segments join

junk food: food which is thought to have little nutritional value, such as chips, etc.

K

kidneys: a pair of bean-shaped glandular organs, situated at the back of the abdominal cavity, which excrete urine

L

legumes: plants that bear their seeds in pods, such as peas and beans

lethargy: the state of being drowsy or lacking in energy; sluggish, apathetic

lethargic: relating to lethargy; drowsy, sluggish

lifestyle: the type of life chosen by an individual or group

ligament: a band of tissue which serves to connect bones or hold organs in place

lungs: two saclike respiratory organs in the thorax of humans and the higher vertebrates

M

menu: a list of the dishes served at a meal

minerals: a substance occurring in nature with a definite chemical composition

muscles: a group of fibers which enable movement

N

nerves: one or more bundles of fibers forming part of the system which conveys impulses of sensation, motion, etc., between the brain or spinal cord and other parts of the body

nervous system: the system of nerves and nerve centers in a human or animal

nutrient: nourishing; providing goodness or nutriment

nutrition: the act or process of nourishing or being nourished; food; nutriment

nutritional label: a table on the packaging of a food product which supplies details of what the food contains

O

obese: excessively fat

obesity: the state of being excessively fat

Glossary of terms

O

overweight: extra or excess weight; weighing more than normal

oxygen: a colorless, odorless gaseous element, constituting about one-fifth of the volume of the atmosphere and present in a combined state in nature; vital for aerobic respiration

P

pedometer: an instrument for recording the number of steps taken in walking, showing the total distance traveled

peer pressure: pressure from friends or workmates to behave in a prescribed manner

perspiration: the act or process of perspiring; sweating; sweat

physical activity: activity which requires the use of the body

preservative: a substance used to keep food fresh or extend life

processed food: food which has been changed or modified

protein: a common name given to the food group which contains meat, fish, eggs, cheese, milk, yogurt, etc.

R

relaxation: a state of relief of the body or mind from effort or application; a diversion or entertainment

respiration: the act of respiring; inhaling and exhaling air; breathing

S

sedentary: requiring a sitting posture; seldom moving about; lack of physical activity

self-esteem: favorable opinion of oneself

skeleton: the bones of a human or animal joined together to form a framework which supports the organs, muscles, tissues, etc.

skin cancer: a tumor or melanoma occurring on the skin

snack: a small portion of food or drink; a light meal usually eaten between main meals

social skills: skills or attributes which enable a person to work or associate well with other people

sodium: a soft, silver-white metallic element which oxidizes rapidly in moist air. Sodium chloride is the chemical name for table salt.

spinal cord: the cord of nervous tissue extending through the spinal column

sport: an activity pursued for exercise or pleasure, usually requiring some form of physical expertise or competence

stress: to emphasize, to worry about, to attach importance or significance upon something

stroke: a sudden interruption of blood supply to the brain caused by a hemorrhage, thrombosis, or embolism

sugar: a sweet crystalline substance, derived mainly from the sugar cane or sugar beet plant, extensively used when cooking

HEALTHY CHOICES

Glossary of terms

S

sweat: to excrete excess watery fluid through the pores of the skin, as from heat or exertion, etc.; perspire; perspiration

system: a combination of body parts which, when joined, form a whole; for example, respiratory system, circulatory system

T

takeout: a meal which is usually purchased from a food outlet and taken away to be eaten

tendon: a band of tough, white tissue which connects a muscle with a bone

training: drill; education; to make fit by regular exercise and diet

U

unhealthy: not healthy; not having good health

V

vitamins: any of a group of food factors essential in small amounts to sustain life; the absence of any one of them results in a deficiency disease

volleyball: a game played in a gymnasium or outdoors with a large ball being struck by hand or arm from side to side over a high net. The ball is not to hit the ground.

W

wastes: products eliminated from the body and considered to be of no further use

Y

yoga: a series of movements or postures "used" or "assigned" to develop flexibility and relaxation skills

HEALTHY EATING PLAN

Name

Date

Breakfast

Healthy snack

Lunch

Healthy snack

Dinner

Tally of the number of glasses of water drunk

BALANCED DIET PLAN

Name

Date

salad	bread, pasta, rice, cereal, noodles	vegetables	fruit	meat, poultry, fish, legumes, eggs, nuts	milk, yogurt, cheese	water
Breakfast						
Lunch						
Dinner						
Snacks						

www.worldteacherspress.com

HEALTHY RECIPE

Name

Date

Recipe name:

Equipment you will need:

Ingredients you will need:

What to do:

Make your recipe, with the help of an adult if necessary.

How does it taste?

Could you follow the steps easily? | YES | NO | SOMETIMES |

EXERCISE DIARY

Name

Day	What did you do?	How long did you do it?	Who did it with you?
Monday _____ date			
Tuesday _____ date			
Wednesday _____ date			
Thursday _____ date			
Friday _____ date			
Saturday _____ date			
Sunday _____ date			
Other activities			

FOOD AND EXERCISE DIARY

Name

	Food				Exercise
	Breakfast	Lunch	Dinner	Snacks	Type/Time spent
Monday _____ date					
Tuesday _____ date					
Wednesday _____ date					
Thursday _____ date					
Friday _____ date					
Saturday _____ date					
Sunday _____ date					

www.worldteacherspress.com ©World Teachers Press®

HEALTHY GOALS PLAN

Name

Date

Type of goal: ☐ Exercise ☐ Diet

My goal is:

To reach my goal, I could:

I will reach my goal on this date:

Draw a picture or explain how you will reward yourself for reaching your goal. Make sure it isn't unhealthy!

A HEALTHY LIFESTYLE

WHAT IS A HEALTHY LIFESTYLE?

Indicators

- Understands the meaning of a healthy lifestyle.
- Reads and completes information on healthy lifestyles.

Teacher information

- It is important that students learn the habits of a healthy lifestyle from an early age. For any of us, changing bad habits is harder than not starting them in the first place! If students follow good examples before they are old enough to make their own decisions, they are more likely to continue with these good habits. For many reasons, students do not have healthy lifestyles. Fast food convenience, preferred sedentary activities, and concerns about playing away from the home without adult supervision all contribute to the current downward trend in childhood health and fitness.

- While there are many role models who advocate healthy lifestyles, students need to experience the benefits of good health for themselves. It is important for the adults in their lives, parents and teachers, to educate them to live healthy lives.

  In school, students are influenced strongly by their peers. It is possible to use this pressure in a positive way by providing an environment which puts the theory of healthy living into practice.

- Read and discuss the information at the top of the page with the students. They can work independently or in pairs to complete the cloze activity.

Additional activities

- Plan a weekly timetable with realistic goals for including more exercise.
- Look through supermarket advertisements and plan a healthy shopping list for a week.
- Plan before-and-after school activities. Include organization and all resources required.

Answers

(A) 1. fuel	2. healthy	3. water	4. decay
(B) 1. muscles	2. hearts	3. properly	4. better
(C) 1. grow	2. recover	3. enjoy	4. music

What is a Healthy Lifestyle?

Good health means being free from sickness and disease, so a healthy lifestyle is one which keeps us that way. If we are healthy, we feel good within our bodies and about ourselves.

The three things which have the greatest effect on our health are:

- *the food and drink we consume.*
- *the amount of exercise we do.*
- *the amount of sleep and relaxation we have.*

Read the words below. Then complete each paragraph by choosing the correct words to fill in the blanks.

(A)

healthy	decay	water	fuel

It is important to eat regular meals to provide the body with enough

_____[1] for a _____[2] lifestyle. Drink enough

_____[3] to keep your body working properly. Avoid

sugary, soft drinks as they can cause tooth _____[4].

(B)

hearts	properly	better	muscles

We need to exercise often to develop our _____[1], especially our

_____[2]. Our internal organs need us to be active so they

can work _____[3]. Even if it's hard work while

we're doing it, we feel _____[4] after we've exercised.

(C)

recover	grow	enjoy	music

We need sleep for our bodies to _____[1] and to

_____[2] from the day's activities. Relaxing gives us the

opportunity to _____[3] less active things like reading, talking

to family and friends, and listening to _____[4].

HEALTH CHALLENGE

Make one positive change to your lifestyle to make it healthier.

BENEFITS OF A HEALTHY LIFESTYLE

A HEALTHY LIFESTYLE

Indicators

- Reads about the physical effects of a healthy lifestyle.
- Learns which elements need to be in balance for a lifestyle to be healthy.

Teacher information

- If students are aware of the personal, physical benefits of healthy living, they will be more aware of positive changes that occur as they improve their lifestyles.

  The digestive system plays an important role in how we feel on the inside and look on the outside. How it functions is directly related to the food and drink we consume. A healthy diet, including plenty of water, promotes the efficiency of this system.

  Exercise also has a beneficial effect on the digestive system. It is more active and functions better than when no exercise is performed. Waste products are removed more regularly, leaving the body more comfortable and lively.

  Less obvious to the students is the role sleep plays in growth and regeneration of cell tissue. They need to appreciate that the body needs sufficient sleep.

  Something we have less control over is the air we breathe. Traffic fumes and industrial pollution are hazards which affect many of us but are, for the most part, out of our control. Passive smoking is something we can avoid. If people at home smoke, it may be hard for the students to alter the situation, but they could offer healthier alternatives such as only smoking outside.

- Read the text with the students before they complete the word search. Explain any words they may not understand.

Additional activities

- Students write a "Healthy lifestyle" acrostic poem, including as many positive aspects as they can.
- Make a list of favorite activities. Categorize them as active or sedentary. Draw a balance scale with active and sedentary activities in each pan. Which type of activity do students do the most?
- Research the function of the digestive system. With a partner, draw an outline of the body and sketch in where the digestive organs are located. Draw arrows to indicate the passage of food. At each organ, briefly explain what happens and what changes occur.

Answers

D	N	U	T	R	I	E	N	T	S	X	A	R	R	E
G	R	O	W	I	N	G	F	R	E	S	H	E	E	X
S	H	I	N	Y	B	O	R	G	A	N	S	L	P	E
L	E	E	N	D	O	R	P	H	I	N	S	A	A	R
B	A	S	F	K	F	X	Y	A	O	N	T	X	I	C
R	L	L	T	H	D	O	P	I	X	A	R	A	R	I
I	T	E	E	T	H	S	O	R	Y	I	O	T	I	S
G	H	E	E	Y	E	S	K	D	G	L	N	I	N	E
H	Y	P	B	L	O	O	D	I	E	S	G	O	G	O
T	G	A	I	R	B	A	L	A	N	C	E	N	M	D

4

Benefits of a Healthy Lifestyle

*A healthy lifestyle is all about **balance**—the right amount of **food**, **drink**, **exercise**, **sleep** and **relaxation**.*

*A well-balanced diet provides all the essential **nutrients** needed for a healthy body. On the inside, the **organs** will work efficiently, making us feel better. On the outside, we will look good, with **bright eyes**, **shiny hair**, **healthy skin**, and **strong teeth** and **nails**.*

*When we exercise, the brain releases **endorphins**, which make us feel good.*

*During sleep the body is busy **growing** and **repairing** damage caused by daily activities.*

***Fresh air** is important for healthy lungs, which send **oxygen** into the bloodstream. If the air we breathe is polluted, our **blood** will be affected and so will our health.*

Find the highlighted words in the word search.

D	N	U	T	R	I	E	N	T	S	X	A	R	R	E
G	R	O	W	I	N	G	F	R	E	S	H	E	E	X
S	H	I	N	Y	B	O	R	G	A	N	S	L	P	E
L	E	E	N	D	O	R	P	H	I	N	S	A	A	R
B	A	S	F	K	F	X	Y	A	O	N	T	X	I	C
R	L	L	T	H	D	O	P	I	X	A	R	A	R	I
I	T	E	E	T	H	S	O	R	Y	I	O	T	I	S
G	H	E	E	Y	E	S	K	D	G	L	N	I	N	E
H	Y	P	B	L	O	O	D	I	E	S	G	O	G	O
T	G	A	I	R	B	A	L	A	N	C	E	N	M	D

A HEALTHY LIFESTYLE

HOW HEALTHY IS MY LIFESTYLE?

Indicators

- Looks critically at his/her own lifestyle.
- Considers positive changes that could be made.

Teacher information

- When discussing this worksheet, it is important that students feel secure enough to be honest about their current lifestyle. It is potentially a very sensitive subject and needs to be handled with diplomacy. For change to occur, the students must not feel they are being judged for their present habits, but applauded for their willingness to change, if necessary.

- The students need to appreciate the importance of balance in their lives. Excesses in any direction are unhealthy. It is not expected that they do not relax during their day but they may be guided into being more selective in their choice of sedentary, relaxing activities.

- The answers to the lifestyle questions on the worksheet would best be completed independently and kept personal.

Additional activities

- Make a list of relaxing activities other than watching TV and using the computer.
- Work with a group of friends to plan healthy activities after school.
- Plan a healthy evening meal for the whole family.

Answers

Teacher check

©World Teachers Press®

How Healthy Is My Lifestyle?

We may not realize how healthy or unhealthy our lifestyles are until we take a close look at them. Complete the questions. Good luck!

1. (a) In the boxes below, write the things you **usually** eat during the day.

morning

afternoon

evening

   (b) Check which phrase best suits your eating habits
      A. well-balanced and healthy ☐
      B. a mixture of healthy and unhealthy ☐
      C. unhealthy ☐

2. (a) In the boxes below, write the exercise in which you **usually** take part.

morning

afternoon

evening

   (b) Check which phrase best suits the exercise you do.
      A. plenty of exercise ☐
      B. some exercise ☐
      C. not very much exercise ☐

3. Which phrase best suits your sleeping routine?
   A. at least ten hours sleep each night ☐
   B. between six and ten hours sleep each night ☐
   C. less than six hours each night ☐

4. (a) How healthy is your lifestyle?
   _____

   (b) How can you improve it?
   _____
   _____
   _____
   _____
   _____

HEALTH CHALLENGE

Limit your time watching TV or playing on the computer to fit in more exercise.

A HEALTHY LIFESTYLE

WHAT FACTORS AFFECT A HEALTHY LIFESTYLE?

Indicators

- Considers possible reasons why our lifestyles are becoming less healthy.
- Considers the role played by the media in promoting healthy lifestyles.

Teacher information

- Highlighting the three statements in Question 1 will raise the awareness of students that their lifestyles may not be healthy. Unless their lives have recently altered, they will assume that the way they live is the norm. For any statement, they may be able to provide a valid reason why it is so. The message they need to appreciate is that balance is the key to a healthy lifestyle. The media has a role to play in promoting a healthy lifestyle.
- Discuss the information about the factors affecting a healthy lifestyle at the top of the worksheet with the students.
- They can complete the questions individually or in pairs. Share answers with the class.

Additional activities

- Students record all car trips for one week. Discuss with their family which regular car trips could be replaced with walking.
- Complete a year group survey on how many students take part in organized sports.
- **"Smoking should be banned in all public places."** Think about this statement and write reasons for and against it. Share views with the class.

Answers

1. Possible answers:
   (a) Fast food is readily available, takes little or no time to prepare
   (b) We travel by car to save time as we have busy lives; parents need to get to work; suburbs are spread out and far from stores and places of interest; some parents consider it safer for their children
   (c) Fewer people are taking part in organized sports because it requires commitment; problems with transportation to venues; rising costs; preference for other activities; local sports organizations not yet established

2. Possible answers:
   Advertisements for stop smoking campaigns; local fun runs; healthy option foods

What Factors Affect a Healthy Lifestyle?

- *The environment in which we live has a great impact upon the lifestyles we lead.*
- *Greater distances between our homes and the places we visit mean we are more likely to use the car rather than walk.*
- *Our lives are busier now so we often eat fast food to save on cooking time.*
- *There are many more computer games, DVDs and programs on TV for us to enjoy, so many people do not wish to spend time playing sports.*
- *It is acceptable to eat junk food, watch TV, play computer games and stay up late occasionally, but we should be aiming to achieve a healthy lifestyle for most of the time.*

1. Give a reason why each statement may be true.

    (a) We eat too much fast food and junk food.

    _____

    _____

    (b) We travel everywhere by car.

    _____

    _____

    (c) Fewer people are taking part in organized sports.

    _____

    _____

We are influenced by what we see, hear and read on TV, radio and in newspapers and magazines, so the media has an important role in spreading the healthy lifestyle message.

2. Write three things you have seen or heard in the media promoting a healthy lifestyle.

    (a) _____

    _____

    (b) _____

    _____

    (c) _____

    _____

HEALTH CHALLENGE

Walk with an adult to places a short distance away that you would usually go to by car.

CHOICES

Indicators

- Appreciates that healthy choices are often available.
- Understands the need to take responsibility for personal choices, even if a healthy example is not being set.

Teacher information

- It is easy to take a passive role and allow someone else to make decisions for us. Students need to be aware that in many instances, they do have the option to choose.

  Their choices may put them in the minority, which may make them feel uncomfortable, even insecure. If they can learn early on to make their own choices, irrespective of others, they will be more prepared to withstand peer pressure at a later stage when more serious issues are involved. Opportunities for recognizing options and making decisions free of external influences should be presented to the students whenever possible.

  Good examples to follow may be helping one another, encouraging healthy lifestyle habits, caring for one another and those less fortunate, helping charities, volunteer work, and being generous, friendly and happy.

  Bad examples to follow may be unhealthy lifestyle practices, bullying, stealing, speeding, using bad language, and showing threatening behavior.

- After discussion, students should complete Question 1 individually.

- For Questions 2 and 3, the examples and choices may apply to wider issues. In the broader sense, the term healthy lifestyle applies beyond the physical and physiological. The extent to which social, moral and ethical aspects are covered depends largely upon the experiences and readiness of the students.

Additional activities

- Compile a list of alternative choices in different lifestyle categories, similar to Question 1. Ask the class to complete the choices anonymously. Analyze the results to determine how healthy classmates are.

- Students draw up a plan of healthy lifestyle options for their own family situation. Challenge their family to be healthy!

- Prepare a talk on the importance of making their own decisions without being influenced by others and present it to the class.

Answers

Teacher check

Choices

Sometimes, we have to do as others ask us or whatever most people want, but there are many more times when we are free to make our own choices about things.

1. What choices would you make in the following examples? Check the box.

    (a)   chocolates, chips and cookies ☐   or fresh fruit and vegetables ☐

    (b)   watching TV ☐   or flying a kite ☐

    (c)   staying up late watching movies ☐   or getting up early for a walk ☐

    (d)   talking with family and friends ☐   or using a computer ☐

Our lifestyle choices are often influenced by other people, such as family and friends. They may also be influenced by TV, sports and music personalities. Some people set good examples to follow, others do not.

2. How has each group of people influenced you? You may leave some sections blank if they do not apply.

	Good examples	Bad examples
Family		
Friends		
Celebrities		

We may make the wrong choices because we don't want to be different from our friends. Write about one of these times.

3. What happened and how did you feel about it?

_____

_____

_____

_____

HEALTH CHALLENGE

Keep a personal tally of the times you choose a healthy snack instead of an unhealthy snack.

HEALTHY CHOICES

WHAT CAN I DO TO IMPROVE MY LIFESTYLE?

Indicators

- Understands that goals need to be realistic and practical if they are to be successful.

- Appreciates that for changes to be made, we must **want** to change.

Teacher information

- For a successful transition to a healthy lifestyle, changes must be practical and easy to maintain. Small changes, introduced over a period of time, will fit more easily into any lifestyle than major changes implemented all at once. The latter approach is unrealistic and will invariably end in failure.

- As students start to experience the benefits of their healthy regimes, they will be motivated to continue. It is important to keep the momentum going at this time. This may be done by having charts for them to record their progress and having some time allocated each week for discussion and sharing of ideas. If before-and after-school activities have been introduced, they must continue and develop so that interest is maintained. Regular "healthy lifestyle" weeks could be organized during the year.

- Discuss what the students are expected to do on the worksheet and make them aware of some of the suggestions above. Students should complete the activities independently.

Additional activities

- Students make personal motivational "star charts." Each time students do something healthy, they give themselves a star. They decide how many stars they must achieve before a reward of their own choice.

- Students choose one of their successful changes from Question 2 on the worksheet. Explain why they originally chose it and why they think it was successful. Present reasons to the class.

- Research the sporting career of a famous athlete of their choice.

Answers

Teacher check

What Can I Do to Improve My Lifestyle?

Very few of us have a perfectly healthy lifestyle. There's room for improvement for all of us. Some things are easy to change, while others are more difficult.

1. Make a list of things you would like to improve. Check whether it would be easy or difficult to change them.

Things I would like to change	Easy to change	Difficult to change

2. For each day of the week, choose one positive change you could make to your lifestyle. Now try them!

   At the end of the week, record how successful you were in achieving these changes.

	Change to be made	Successful?
Monday		
Tuesday		
Wednesday		
Thursday		
Friday		
Saturday		
Sunday		

HEALTH CHALLENGE

Work harder on one of the changes in Question 2 in which you were not as successful.

EFFECTS OF AN UNHEALTHY LIFESTYLE

Indicators

- Understands the implications of an unhealthy lifestyle.
- Reads and completes information on unhealthy lifestyles.

Teacher information

- The students may have already experienced some symptoms asked for in Question 1; for example, tooth decay, gum disease, increased weight, excessive sweating and breathlessness, aching muscles, sore joints, and a lack of strength, stamina and suppleness.

- Some of these symptoms can occur in a fit and healthy person after a period of high-level, sustained exercise, but the body will return to normal quickly. In the unfit person, they will occur after a short period of low-level exercise, and the body takes a much longer time to recover.

- Many students may know people who are suffering from any of the conditions mentioned. (Note that type 2 diabetes is a lifestyle disease which can usually be prevented. Type 1 diabetes cannot be prevented.) While it is important to speak sensitively about these issues, it may be possible to use these people as a resource for information and interviews. Meeting someone with a health problem may make the students more aware of the reality of such a condition.

- Teaching basic human biology will help students appreciate what happens when we eat and exercise and why it is important to keep healthy.

- Read and discuss the information with the students before they complete the cloze.

Additional activities

- Research the function of a major organ of the human body. Explain what it needs to stay healthy and efficient. Describe what can happen when it becomes unhealthy.

- Make a list of favorite foods, then categorize them as healthy or unhealthy. Share lists with the class.

Answers

(A)	1. food	2. fuel	3. fat	4. overweight	5. obese
(B)	1. better	2. diseases	3. avoided	4. heart disease	5. diabetes
(C)	1. muscle	2. stronger	3. exercise	4. stroke	
(D)	1. soft	2. juices	3. high	4. sparingly	5. decay
	6. cleaned				

Effects of an Unhealthy Lifestyle

We often don't realize how unhealthy we have become until we start getting signs from our bodies; for example, tooth decay and becoming short of breath after mild exercise.
What happens to our bodies if we treat them badly?

Choose the correct words to fill the gaps.

(A)

food	obese	fuel	overweight	fat

The _____[1] we eat provides us with the _____[2] we need for the activity we do. Any leftover fuel is stored in the body as _____[3]. If we regularly take in more fuel than we need, we will become _____[4]. If we become very overweight, we are said to be _____[5].

better	heart disease	diseases	diabetes	avoided

B)

Unfortunately, many people look after their cars _____[1] than their bodies, and as a result, they suffer from _____[2] which could be _____,[3] such as _____[4] and _____[5] (type 2).

stronger	stroke	muscle	exercise

(C)

The heart is a _____[1] which pumps blood around the body, and like all muscles, it will get _____[2] with exercise. If it does not have enough _____[3], it may not be strong enough to cope with strain, and a _____[4] or a heart attack could be the result.

high	decay	cleaned	sparingly	soft	juices

(D)

_____[1] drinks and some fruit _____[2] have a _____[3] concentration of sugar and should be drunk _____[4]. Tooth _____[5] is very common in people who have a lot of sugar in their diet. Teeth need to be _____[6] regularly, especially after meals.

HEALTH CHALLENGE

Clean your teeth after each meal and at bedtime.

HEALTHY CHOICES

PLANNING FOR A HEALTHY LIFESTYLE WEEK

Indicators

- Uses personal knowledge and research to make suggestions for a healthy lifestyle awareness week.

- Demonstrates an understanding of why we need to have a healthy lifestyle.

Teacher information

- Just as the students need to be ready and willing to change to a healthy lifestyle, so they must be proactive in the planning of activities to promote it. The more they make the project their own, at home as well as at school, the more likely they are to succeed.

- Students could complete this activity in pairs or a small group.

Additional activities

- Design a poster to promote awareness within the school of the benefits of a healthy lifestyle. Display the posters around the school.

- Make a collage of healthy foods, using pictures cut from magazines.

- Research local sports organizations. Make a directory of these organizations for the students to refer to, including contact numbers, training nights, age groups and any other relevant information.

Answers

Teacher check

Planning for a Healthy Lifestyle Week

1. Make a list of ideas for activities you could suggest for a healthy lifestyle awareness week. Use the headings below.

Lunchbox contents	
Recess activities	
After school activities	
Relaxation activities	

2. Prepare a talk about the importance of developing a healthy lifestyle. Use the following ideas to help plan your talk.

    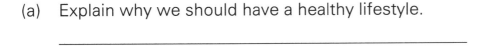

    (a) Explain why we should have a healthy lifestyle.

    _____

    _____

    (b) Describe a healthy eating and drinking plan.

    _____

    _____

    (c) Make suggestions for increasing daily exercise.

    _____

    _____

    (d) Describe the benefits you will notice from these changes.

    _____

    _____

3. Present your talk to the class.

    HEALTH CHALLENGE

    Take part in preparing the weekly shopping list. Ask for healthier options where possible.

A HEALTHY LIFESTYLE

HOW CAN I HELP?

Indicators

- Appreciates that all movement can be described as exercise, but that some exercises are more strenuous than others.

- Considers the requirements for an active family outing.

Teacher information

- It is important for students to realize that their lives can be made healthier by making small changes that fit easily into their normal routines. Even a ten-minute active chore before sitting down in front of the TV is an improvement! Leisure time should include both active and sedentary activities. If students are taught how to manage their time, they will learn how to create a balance between all areas of their lives.

  Doing chores around the home not only provides incidental exercise, but also benefits the whole family and will surely be much appreciated.

- Students should complete this activity independently.

Additional activities

- Make a list of jobs students do around the school.

  Which exercises, from the worksheet, do they cover?

- Using pictures from magazines, make a collage of different activities. List each activity and devise a word search for others to complete.

- Research old schoolyard games that parents and grandparents used to play. Share them with the class and learn how to play some of them.

Answers

1. Students should discover that most of the chores require all four movements.

2–3. Teacher check

How Can I Help?

Exercise is not just about playing organized sports or running around at the park. Helping with the housework can be a great physical workout too. Try it and see!

1. Think about the movement required to complete each household chore in the box below. Draw lines from each movement to any chore that requires that movement.

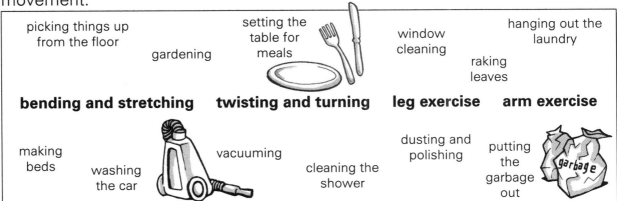

picking things up from the floor

setting the table for meals

window cleaning

hanging out the laundry

gardening

raking leaves

bending and stretching   **twisting and turning**   **leg exercise**   **arm exercise**

making beds

washing the car

vacuuming

cleaning the shower

dusting and polishing

putting the garbage out

garbage

2. Make up a weekly schedule of chores you could do at home to help yourself and your family and get more exercise at the same time.

Monday	
Tuesday	
Wednesday	
Thursday	
Friday	
Saturday	
Sunday	

3. Plan an active family outing such as a picnic or hike. List the resources you will need.

HEALTH CHALLENGE

Do at least one active household chore each day. You will get some exercise and help mom or dad at the same time!

HOW DO YOU MANAGE YOUR DAY?

Indicators

- Outlines how he/she spends the day.
- Looks critically at his/her management of time.

Teacher information

- Seeing a visual representation of a well-managed day and comparing it with his/her own will make the student more aware of how much time is given to each aspect of his/her life. Students will see the big blocks of time taken up with sleep and school and realize that less than one third is left for them to manage.

- We can guide students in the use of their leisure time but ultimately the choice is theirs. Providing a checklist of essential things may help; e.g., meal times and showering. Some students may require more guidance, so suggestions for management of time may be needed; for example, playing at the park, going swimming, reading, playing board games, listening to music, household chores, helping with shopping, meal preparation and clearing away afterwards.

- If the students have the support of their adult caregivers and peers, they will find a healthy lifestyle easier to establish and maintain.

Additional activities

- Make a display of the clocks students complete in Question 2, showing how each student spends a typical day.

- Students choose one aspect of their day that needs adjusting, explaining what they intend to do to improve it. Share their goal with the class.

- Students begin a diary, including how they spend their leisure time. At the end of each week, write a comment about how they feel their healthy lifestyle journey is going.

Answers

Teacher check

How Do You Manage Your Day?

1. Look at the first clock. It shows a day in the life of a healthy student including the food and beverages consumed for meals and snacks.

2. Complete this clock to show a typical school day for you.

3. Discuss how your clock compares to the one above.

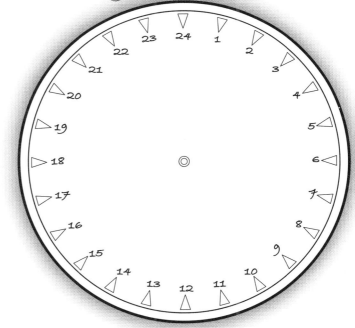

HEALTH CHALLENGE

Manage your time so that your day has a balance between active and sedentary activities.

HEALTHY EATING

A HEALTHY DIET

Indicators

- Reads information about a healthy diet.
- Recognizes the different food groups that are required to maintain a balanced diet.

Teacher information

- The *Healthy Eating Guide* (see diagram on page 23) shows the foods needed for a healthy diet. The foods in the largest segment should provide the main part of our diet; the requirements get smaller as shown. Food servings eaten from each part of the guide each day should provide people with enough nutrients and energy to help them grow and keep healthy.
- The main food groups include:

  – *bread, cereals, rice, noodles, pasta.* This group provides carbohydrates, protein, fiber, some fat, iron and thiamin, magnesium, zinc, riboflavin, niacin equivalents, folate and sodium. Wholemeal and multigrain varieties contain more nutrients than white products, which are more highly processed.

  – *vegetables and legumes.* This group supplies vitamin A (beta-carotene), carbohydrates, fiber, magnesium, iron, vitamin C, folate and potassium.

  – *fruit.* This group provides vitamins (especially vitamin C), carbohydrates, fiber and folate. Fruit is sweet because of the natural sugar it contains. Dried fruit also belongs in this group, but it contains concentrated forms of sugar and should be eaten in smaller quantities.

  – *milk, yogurt, cheese.* This group provides calcium, protein, energy, fat, cholesterol, carbohydrates, magnesium, zinc, riboflavin, vitamin B12, sodium and potassium. There are many varieties in this group, including fresh, dried, evaporated and longlife products. The most important factor concerning this group is that it is the best source of calcium for healthy bones and teeth.

  – *meat, fish, poultry, eggs, nuts, legumes.* This group provides protein, iron, zinc, fat, cholesterol, niacin equivalents and vitamin B12. Iron supplements may be needed for vegetarians and those people who do not eat red meat.

  – *fats, oils and sugars* are not separately essential to our diet and should only be eaten in small amounts. Fats may be unsaturated, such as those in oils and margarines. Some may be beneficial in lowering cholesterol levels in the blood. Saturated fats can increase the risk of heart disease. They can be found in butter, lard and drippings. Sugar has little nutritional value, so foods with a high sugar content, such as soft drinks, candy, jams, honey, cakes and cookies, should be eaten in small quantities and considered "occasional treats."

  Individual and family eating patterns are greatly influenced by personal, social and cultural practices. Other factors which influence a healthy diet include time constraints and the skills needed to prepare and cook food.

- Read and discuss the information about the *Healthy Eating Guide* with the students.
- Students can work independently to answer Questions 1 to 5.

Additional activities

- Create a menu for breakfast, lunch and dinner that provides a balanced diet.
- Use the word "BALANCED" to create an acrostic poem about healthy eating.
- Students design a "healthy sandwich." Hold a competition where students can make and discuss their healthy creations. Organize healthy snack treats as rewards.

Answers

1. Teacher check
2. (a) bread, cereal, rice, pasta and noodles   (b) oils, fats, sweets
3–5. Teacher check

Healthy Eating

Food is fuel for the human body. Everybody needs to have a well-balanced diet made up of a variety of foods from different food groups. Choosing the right foods to eat helps build our bones and muscles, helps us to grow, aids our organs, and gives us energy. The Healthy Eating Guide *shows how much of each food you should eat.*

1. Color the foods from the chart you like to eat.

2. Which foods should we eat …
   (a) the most of?

   _____

   _____

   _____

   _____

   _____

   (b) in very small amounts?

   _____

   _____

3. List two of your favorite foods. To which food group do you think they belong?

Favorite foods	Food group
_____	_____
_____	_____

4. What could you do to make your eating habits healthier?

   _____

   _____

5. How do you feel after eating …

healthy food?	junk food?

HEALTH CHALLENGE

Drink more water and milk throughout the week as these are a healthier choice than sugary fruit juices and soft drinks.

A BALANCED DIET

A HEALTHY DIET

Indicators

- Records diet data for one day.

- Identifies healthy aspects of his/her diet.

- Identifies ways to make his/her own diet healthier.

Teacher information

- Students will need a copy of the worksheet on page 25 to complete at home. Try to record food intake over a weekend day as this is often different from weekly food routines. Students could repeat the exercise on a weekday and compare.

- After collecting the information, students should be able to identify which food groups they have eaten that day and those groups from which they have not eaten enough.

- Review the *Healthy Eating Guide* (see page 23), and discuss the importance of balancing the food groups for a healthy diet.

- Allow students time to highlight meals on their diary which were healthy and to complete their self-evaluation.

- Discuss meals which could be improved. Discuss ways students could improve their diets, such as choosing fruit, carrot sticks and dried fruits as healthy alternatives to sweet, fatty snacks, or choosing to drink milk or water rather than soft drinks or juices.

Additional activities

- Make healthy snacks to share in class.

- Develop a recipe book of healthy meals and snacks from students' families. Collate and allow students to borrow it to take home.

- Students collect and cut pictures of ten different foods from newspapers, magazines, or junk mail. Glue them onto paper to make a balanced diet for the day. Write the price of each item as found in the newspaper. At which meal would they choose to eat these foods? Put a check next to the foods that are healthy and cross out those that are unhealthy.

Answers

Teacher check

Self-evaluation

- Is it a balanced diet?

  YES   NO

- Do you eat more junk food on the weekend?

  YES   NO

- Which was your healthiest meal?

  _____

- Which food group do you need to eat ...

  more from?

  _____

  less from?

  _____

- Do you drink six to eight glasses of water per day?

  YES   NO

A Balanced Diet

	Bread, cereal, rice, pasta, noodles	Vegetables	Fruit	Meat, poultry, fish, legumes, eggs, nuts	Milk, yogurt, cheese	Fats, oils, sweets	Water
BREAKFAST							
LUNCH							
DINNER							
SNACKS							

HEALTH CHALLENGE

Make one meal you eat this week healthier.

BENEFITS OF A HEALTHY DIET

A HEALTHY DIET

Indicators

- Identifies the benefits of a healthy diet.

- Identifies the way to make his/her diet more healthy.

Teacher information

- There are seven different types of nutrients that the body requires: vitamins, minerals, water, protein, fats, carbohydrates and dietary fiber. Nutrients regulate the body processes and provide energy for healthy bones and muscles.

- It is important for students to understand that eating a balanced diet will help them to achieve an active and healthy lifestyle. The importance here is a balance of the different food groups. Patterns of eating too little or too much of one food group should be discouraged from an early age, as they can lead to problems later.

- Some healthy eating guidelines include:

  – Eat fresh food rather than processed food.

  – Eat a variety of different foods.

  – Avoid fatty meats.

  – Avoid eating too many sweet foods.

  – Eat only until you are comfortably full.

  – Drink six to eight glasses of water per day.

- Read and discuss the information with the students.

- Students can work independently to complete Questions 1 to 3.

Additional activities

- Ask students to make a list of their favorite foods. Have them draw each food, then decide what type of fuel it contains what use the body has for that food.

- Plan a well-balanced menu to feed a family for a week.

- In small groups, brainstorm to list the types of foods eaten for a special occasion like a birthday party or a holiday. Make another list showing healthier food choices for the same event.

Answers

1. (a) vegetables, legumes and fruit
   (b) dairy; vegetables, legumes and fruit
   (c) bread, cereal, rice, pasta, noodles; dairy
   (d) meat, fish, eggs, nuts; bread, cereal, rice, pasta, noodles

2. Possible answers
   (a) healing; growth; carry oxygen in the blood; healthy bones, skin, teeth and eyes; managing weight
   (b) energy, growth, repair of body, carrying oxygen in the blood, healing

3. Teacher check

26

Benefits of a Healthy Diet

We need to eat a wide variety of foods every day to provide our bodies with important nutrients to keep us healthy. Healthy foods contain essential vitamins, minerals, water, protein, fats, carbohydrates and fiber to help us grow and give us energy.

Like a machine, the human body needs the right fuel to work properly. Healthy food choices fuel our bodies. Unhealthy food choices contain lots of sugar and fat, making it hard for our bodies to fight diseases and making us overweight.

We cannot get all the nutrients we need from just one food, so we must eat a balance of foods from each of the healthy food groups. These foods provide us with what we need to run a healthy body. The chart below explains the benefits of a well-balanced diet.

Food group ...	Provides ...	Important for ...
bread, cereal, rice, pasta, noodles	fiber, vitamins, minerals, carbohydrates and protein	energy, growth, repair of body
vegetables, legumes and fruit	vitamins, fiber, carbohydrates	managing weight, eyes, healthy bones, skin, red blood cells, teeth
dairy	calcium, protein, vitamins	energy, repairing cells, strong bones and teeth
meat, fish, eggs, nuts	iron, zinc, protein	carrying oxygen in the blood, healing, growth

1. Which foods would you eat to help you ...

    (a) manage your weight?

    _____

    (b) build strong bones?

    _____

    (c) have energy to play sports?

    _____

    (d) heal a wound?

    _____

2. What benefits do you think these foods could give you?

    (a)

    (b)

3. Draw a favorite snack food.

    (a) Is it healthy? YES NO

    (b) If not, what would be a better choice?

    (c) How could this healthy snack help your body?

    _____

    _____

HEALTH CHALLENGE

What did you bring for lunch today? Find out how the food in your lunchbox helps your body.

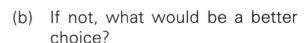

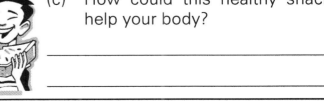

THE IMPORTANCE OF WATER

A HEALTHY DIET

Indicators

- Reads information about the importance of water to our bodies.
- Investigates the water content of different foods.

Teacher information

- Our bodies need a lot of water to function. Each day our body loses up to 12 cups of water (half a cup from the soles of our feet, two to four cups from breathing, two to four cups from perspiration and four to six cups in urine). This needs to be replaced through healthy eating and drinking six to eight glasses of water each day.

  Water:

  - Contains no calories, is fat-free, low in sodium (salt), cholesterol-free and makes you feel full.
  - Helps regulate body temperature through perspiration.
  - Lubricates the joints of our body.
  - Removes wastes (that need to be dissolved in water) from our kidneys.
  - Is essential to brain energy and functions as the brain is made up of 85% water.
  - Stops our body from dehydrating which causes stress and headaches.
  - Moistens our lungs as we breathe in oxygen and give out carbon dioxide.
  - Is essential in the spinal cord which supports the weight of the upper body.

- Read and discuss the information with the students and what they are expected to do on the worksheet.

NOTE: The light source should be at least 20 inches above the food and placed in a safe area.

Additional activities

- Repeat the experiment with other foods or allocate foods to groups of students to investigate and compare results.
- Find out the nutritional value of drinks like soft drinks and fruit juices. Compare the health values to that of water.
- Keep a tally of the amount and types of drinks students have each day. Can they drink more water in a day?

Answers

1–3. Teacher check

4. (Greatest) Probably the apple
   (Least) Probably the banana

5. Weight loss occurred because they lost water.

The Importance of Water

Our bodies are made up of nearly 70% water. Although you can live several weeks without food, you can only survive a few days without water. This is because we constantly lose water through sweating, going to the bathroom and even breathing. The average person needs at least 2.5 quarts of water a day—half from drinks and half from food.

Foods contain different amounts of water; for example, lettuce is made up of 96% water, apples 85%, chicken 75% and cookies 5%.

Follow the task outline below to find out the water content of different foods.

YOU WILL NEED

- A small slice of apple, potato, celery and banana
- Desk lamp (or similar)
- Tray
- Kitchen scales

1. Draw and weigh each slice of food.

apple	potato	celery	banana
_____ ounces	_____ ounces	_____ ounces	_____ ounces

2. Turn on the light and leave the food slices overnight under the lamp.

3. Draw and reweigh the food.

apple	potato	celery	banana
_____ ounces	_____ ounces	_____ ounces	_____ ounces

4. Rank the food in order from the greatest weight loss to the least. Show the weight difference between 1 and 3.

ounces	ounces	ounces	ounces

5. What do you think happened? Explain.

_____

_____

HEALTH CHALLENGE

Drink the recommended six to eight glasses of water at least one day this week.

HEALTHY CHOICES

SNACK ATTACK

Indicators

- Reads information about snack foods.
- Recognizes the differences between healthy and unhealthy snacks.
- Identifies ways to improve his/her snack choices.

Teacher information

- Snacks are normal for children, as they need to refuel to keep up their energy levels for the day's activities. The key to healthy snacking is to balance nutrients, calories and exercise.

- Snacks can be planned "mini-meals" or spontaneous food intake. Foods for snacks can be chosen just as easily from a variety of healthy foods as they can from non-nutritious foods. Wiser snacking decisions are made when snacks are planned or prepared in advance. Snacks eaten at home are usually more nutritious than those eaten away from home or "on the run."

- People often snack mid-morning, in the afternoon, or before bed. They snack at home, in front of the TV, in the car, at events like concerts or games, at school, in the park, or while doing simple tasks. Where and when snacks are eaten can influence the type of snack consumed.

- Snacks should be filling and nutritional. Healthy selections should be made from the *Healthy Eating Guide* groups. They should be eaten for hunger, not to relieve boredom. Snacks eaten before physical activity can boost energy levels.

- Snacks will increase the daily nutrient intake, help maintain blood glucose levels, prevent hunger, help to improve mood swings, improve concentration, prevent emotional eating and can help to control weight. Sweets, as well as foods high in fats, oils and salt should be small additions to our diet rather than excessive portions. Diet problems occur when foods high in sugar, salt and fat are eaten in excess and combined with inactivity.

- Healthy snacks should be low in added salt, sugar and fats, small in portion, and made from fresh instead of processed ingredients. Snack selections should be made based on the *Healthy Eating Guide* and should taste good.

- Read and discuss the information with the students.
- Students should complete the worksheet independently.

Additional activities

- Students find snack food advertisements in magazines and newspapers and use these as models to design their own advertisements for a healthy snack.
- Make simple, healthy snacks in small class groups to share.
- Design a poster to show healthy alternatives to junk food snacks.

Answers

1. Teacher check 3–5. Teacher check
2. Healthy snacks include apple, popcorn, cheese and crackers, and frozen yogurt

Snack Attack!

"Snack attacks" can refuel your body to give you the energy to run, play and work. Eating snacks keeps your brain and body moving. Snacks are "mini-meals," and to be healthy, they should be made from the main food groups from the healthy eating chart. Junk food snacks such as chips, cake and cookies are not as healthy and usually have lots of sugar, salt and fat in them. These foods should only be eaten occasionally. Snacks should be low in fat, low in salt, low in sugars and small in size. Fresh food should be used for snacks, when possible.

1. Draw or name some of your favorite snacks. Circle the healthy choices.

2. Put a check by the healthy snacks. Cross out the less healthy choices.

apple	
bag of chips	
popcorn	
cheese and crackers	
chocolate bar	
frozen yogurt on a stick	

3. What times of the day do you eat snacks?

_____

_____

4. What are some of the things you do when snacking?

_____

_____

5. Write healthy snack choices for each situation.

ⓐ You are asked to bring snacks for your teammates after a game.

ⓑ You and your friends are packing snacks for a morning at the beach.

HEALTH CHALLENGE

While helping with the weekly food shopping, ask if you could buy a healthier new snack to try at home or school.

HEALTHY SNACKS

A HEALTHY DIET

Indicators

- Recognizes what makes a healthy snack.
- Plans, writes and follows a procedure for making a healthy snack.
- Evaluates his/her group's results.

Teacher information

- Healthy snacks should be low in added salt, sugar and fat, small in portion, made from fresh ingredients instead of processed ingredients, made from a variety of foods from the *Healthy Eating Guide* and taste good. The key to healthy snacking is to balance nutrients, calories and exercise. Snacks should be filling and nutritious.
- Divide the class into manageable groups.
- Ensure each group has the equipment and ingredients to make one of the healthy snacks.
- Discuss how each group must first plan the steps needed to make the snack and write up the procedure. Students can then follow their procedure to make the snack.
- Direct students to clean up and complete their evaluation of the recipe.

NOTE: Ensure students have clean hands and utensils when handling and preparing food.

Additional activities

- Collect healthy recipes to make a class booklet.
- Plan and make healthy snacks to suit the occasion; e.g., after a sports match, on a picnic, at the beach, playing after school.
- Research the benefits of eating healthy snacks.

Answers

Teacher check

©World Teachers Press®

Healthy Snacks

In small groups, make one of these healthy snacks.

Fruity popcorn
- popcorn (made following package directions)
- dried fruits (e.g., apples, peaches, dates, raisins, apricots, mangoes) chopped into small pieces
- unsalted nuts (optional)
- knife, cutting board
- large bowl

Bugs on a log
- celery sticks (cut to suitable size)
- cream cheese or peanut butter (for filling the celery sticks)
- raisins (as "bugs" on the "log")
- knives, cutting board

Fruity kebabs
- 3–5 different fruits in season, cut into chunks; e.g., apple, banana, melon, strawberries
- wooden skewers (2–3 per person) with sharp ends removed
- knife, cutting board, small bowl (for dip)
- large tub of yogurt (any flavor) to share among class groups as dipping sauce

Remember:
Have clean hands before handling food.

1. Discuss with your group how you will make one of these recipes.

2. Draw and write the steps you will use below.

①	②	③
④	⑤	⑥

3. Follow the steps to make the snack. Eat and enjoy!

4. (a) How did it taste?

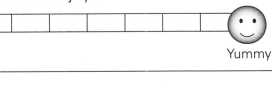

Yucky   Yummy

    (b) Did you follow the steps easily?

      YES   NO

    (c) What could you do to improve the recipe?

HEALTH CHALLENGE

Find and make a healthy snack to pack in your school lunchbox.

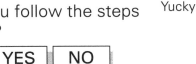

HEALTHY CHOICES

33

NUTRITIONAL INFORMATION LABELS

A HEALTHY DIET

Indicator

- Reads and analyzes a food nutrition label.

Teacher information

- Federal and state laws require food manufacturers to accurately represent what their products contain. Labels on all packaged food must display the following information:
  - Name of the food
  - Name and business address of the manufacturer or importer
  - Country of origin of the food
  - A list of ingredients listed from greatest to smallest by weight (including added water)
  - Warnings about the presence of major allergens in foods, however small the amount
  - Nutrition information panel
  - A use-by date (if a food must be consumed before a certain date for health and safety reasons) or a "best before date" (if the shelf life is less than two years)

- A nutritional label usually lists the main ingredients of the packaged food; the quantities per serving; the number of servings in the package; the energy in calories; the total grams of fat per serving (including saturated fat); the levels of protein, carbohydrates, sugars (both natural and added), dietary fiber and sodium (salt) and cholesterol.

- Trans fats are a specific type of fat. They are formed when liquid oils are made into solid fats such as shortening or hard margarine. Trans fats raise bad cholesterol (LDL) and may be found in foods such as vegetable shortenings, some margarines, crackers, candy, cookies, snack foods, fried and baked foods, and processed foods. Trans fats need not be listed on a label if the total fat content is less than 0.5 gm per serving.

- Food labelling enables shoppers to make informed food choices. By reading the labels, people can select a variety of food products that best suits their nutritional needs.

- For this activity, students will need to collect or have access to a variety of packaged foods with nutrition labels. Students could complete the activity in pairs, small groups, or individually. Discuss and compare results.

Additional activities

- Collect a variety of nutrition labels to share and discuss with the class. Compare the nutritional value of similar foods. Rank the foods in order from healthiest to least healthy.

- Investigate food additives and their purpose in processed foods; for example, preservatives prolong the shelf life of products.

- Research genetically-modified foods.

Answers

Teacher check

Nutritional Information Labels

Most packaged food has a table or panel on the label to tell what the food in the package contains. People can read the nutritional label to make healthier food choices. Food with less than 5 g of fat or sugar per 100 g is reasonably healthy.

1. Collect information from two different packaged foods to complete the nutrition panels below.

    (a) PRODUCT: _____

NUTRITION FACTS	
Servings per package: _____ (____ g)	
Servings Per Container _____	
Amount Per Serving	
Calories _____ Calories from fat _____	
	% Daily Value
Total Fat _____ g	____%
Saturated Fat ____ g	____%
Trans Fat ____ g	____%
Cholesterol ____ mg	____%
Sodium ____ mg	____%
Total Carbohydrate ____ g	____%
Dietary Fiber ____ g	____%
Sugars ____ g	
Protein ____ g	
Vitamin A	____%
Vitamin C	____%
Calcium	____%
Iron	____%

    (b) PRODUCT: _____

NUTRITION FACTS	
Servings per package: _____ (____ g)	
Servings Per Container _____	
Amount Per Serving	
Calories _____ Calories from fat _____	
	% Daily Value
Total Fat _____ g	____%
Saturated Fat ____ g	____%
Trans Fat ____ g	____%
Cholesterol ____ mg	____%
Sodium ____ mg	____%
Total Carbohydrate ____ g	____%
Dietary Fiber ____ g	____%
Sugars ____ g	
Protein ____ g	
Vitamin A	____%
Vitamin C	____%
Calcium	____%
Iron	____%

2. Which food ...

    (a) has more calories per 100 g?

a	b

    (b) has more sugar per 100 g?

a	b

    (c) has more fat per 100 g?

a	b

    (d) is higher in salt per 100 g?

a	b

3. Which food do you think is the healthier choice? Explain.

    _____

    _____

    _____

    _____

HEALTH CHALLENGE

Read the nutritional labels on your favorite snacks and choose one with less fat and sugar.

WHAT WOULD YOU LIKE TO KNOW?

A HEALTHY DIET

Indicator

- Creates own nutritional information label.

Teacher information

- Discuss and list on the board the types of things shown on current nutritional information labels. Check those which the students still feel are important.

- Students offer suggestions for other inclusions such as additives, preservatives, peanut, wheat, and dairy content (for students with allergies), healthy food check, etc.

- Discuss the appearance of the label. Is a rectangle the best shape? Does it stand out enough to be a focus of attention? Should it be more colorful? Is it too cluttered? Should it be bigger?

- Allow students to discuss their creation in pairs before completing the questions and layout.

Additional activities

- Collects interesting food packaging; for inspiration for creating interesting nutritional labels.

- Compose jingles to encourage consumers to view nutritional information labels when shopping.

- Encourage students to find the dictionary meanings of unknown words on panels.

Answers

Teacher check

What Would You Like to Know?

Imagine that you were able to create your own label to put on packaged foods. What would you like to include? Remember that the label aims to help you to choose healthier foods for a healthy diet!

1. Complete the following and explain why you would include each.

    (a) I would like to know:

    *   _____

        _____

    *   _____

        _____

        _____

    *   _____

        _____

    *   _____

        _____

        _____

    *   _____

        _____

    *   _____

        _____

    *   _____

        _____

    *   _____

2. In this box show what your label would look like.

FOOD PACKAGING APPEAL

A HEALTHY DIET

Indicator

- Investigates and compares food packaging for its advertising appeal to the shopper.

Teacher information

- Advertisers want us to buy their products. To accomplish this, they need to grab our attention. Advertisers work on influencing our wants, needs, or feelings to get us to buy or react to their products. With so many products to choose from, advertisers must find a convincing selling message to appeal to shoppers.

  Some of their messages have appeal for:
  - Saving us time or money.
  - Making us feel happy, safe, or loved.
  - Making us healthier.
  - Making us look better.
  - Giving us power or influence.
  - Pleasing our tastebuds.
  - Offering us ease of use or a convenience factor.

- For this activity, students will need to collect or have access to a variety of packaged foods. Students could complete the activity in pairs, small groups, or individually. Discuss and compare results.

Additional activities

- Design a box cover for a new product. What selling messages, target audience, colors and striking features will it need to include to sell the product? Display the finished results for discussion.

- Design a magazine advertisement to promote this new product.

- View TV food commercials to see what catchy phrases, music and methods are used to advertise the products. Record and discuss findings.

Answers

Teacher check

Food Packaging Appeal

Advertisers use many methods to grab the attention of shoppers and to persuade them to buy their products.

1. Collect three different packaged food products. Study the packaging carefully to complete the table.

Product	A	B	C
Food messages on the package; e.g., 90% fat-free, baked not fried			
Other ways the advertiser has tried to appeal to shoppers; e.g., color, characters			
Have you seen this product before?			
If so, where? (e.g., on TV, at the store)			
List a total per 100 g serving for … – fats. – sugar.	_____ g _____ g	_____ g _____ g	_____ g _____ g

2. Which product is the healthiest?

_____

3. Which product appeals to you the most? Explain.

_____
_____
_____
_____

HEALTH CHALLENGE

Name any foods you have bought because of the advertising. Have they been healthy choices? Find a packaged product you like that is also good for you.

JUNK FOOD

Indicators

- Reads information about junk food.

- Analyzes situations that can lead to junk food consumption.

Teacher information

- Diets consisting of junk or fast foods have more fat, sugar and salt than nutrients. Our modern living, with the influences of television, advertisers, peers and a hurried lifestyle, make junk food an easy choice.

- A healthy diet with a variety of good food directly affects our well-being. A person with a healthy body sleeps well, has energy, is alert and bright, maintains a good weight and generally has a happy disposition. An improper diet can have long-term ill effects on our bodies.

- Nobody expects children or adults to always eat healthy food. There is a great variety of foods to sample and enjoy. Junk foods should be considered a treat, to be eaten only occasionally, rather than a regular meal.

- Read and discuss the information with the students.

- Students should complete the activities independently.

Additional activities

- Conduct a classroom survey on favorite takeout foods. Graph the results.

- Cut out and analyze magazine food advertisements. Discuss what appealing features are used by the advertiser to get people to buy their product.

- Design a magazine advertisement to promote a healthy food. Use advertising techniques similar to those used in fast food advertisements to tempt buyers; e.g., catchy messages, inviting, colorful pictures.

Answers

Teacher check

Junk Food

People are spending more money each year on convenience or takeout meals. Junk food and fast food like burgers, french fries, chocolates, soft drinks and ice cream, are now often a regular part of our daily diet. Instead, junk food should be a treat, eaten only occasionally. Diets made up of junk foods have more fat, sugar and salt levels than other nutrients. Too much junk food could mean the body is missing out on important nutrients, which can lead to health problems like obesity, type 2 diabetes, heart disease and tooth decay.

Our busy lifestyle of working, going to school, playing sports and seeing friends makes junk food an easy and quick food choice. Television advertisements and what our friends are eating and drinking can also lead us to make unhealthy food choices.

1. Complete the chart about your favorite junk foods.

Food	Where from?	Eaten mostly on …		Eaten …	
		weekends	**weekdays**	**alone**	**with others**

2. Color the answers. (Some may have more than one.)

    (a) I mostly eat my junk food

at a table	in the store	in front of the TV	with family or friends

    (b) I eat more junk food

alone	with friends	with family

    (c) I am more likely to eat junk food when I am sad or upset. | TRUE | FALSE |

    (d) I eat fast food

once a week	only on weekends	more than once a week

    (e) I like to try new foods advertised on TV. | TRUE | FALSE |

3. When might you eat more junk food than normal?

    _____

    _____

4. (a) Do you think you eat too much junk food? | TRUE | FALSE |

    (b) What could you do to eat less?

    _____

    _____

    _____

HEALTH CHALLENGE

Try making a healthy, homemade burger rather than a fast food burger.

FOOD COMMERCIALS

A HEALTHY DIET

Indicators

- Views and analyzes TV food commercials.

- Shows an understanding that advertisers are trying to influence our decision making.

Teacher information

- Advertising in the media is a powerful influence on health choices made by individuals. Advertisers work on influencing our wants, needs, or feelings to get us to buy their products. Some of their messages have appeal for:
  - Saving us money or time.
  - Making us feel happy, safe, or loved.
  - Making us healthier.
  - Giving us power or influence.
  - Making us look better.
  - Pleasing our tastebuds or hunger.
  - Offering us ease of use or convenience.

- For this activity, students need to view TV food commercials. Discuss with the students how advertisers try to influence our choices with attention-grabbing techniques. To complete the table, students record the name of the products and the advertising message used for each one. They then check the boxes for the influences used for each product. Complete the questions and compare results.

Additional activities

- Tally the number of food commercials during a half-hour children's program on television and discuss the results.

- Create a television commercial for a healthy food that the students like. Groups can perform their commercials in front of the class. Discuss how influenced the audience was to buy their product.

- Survey the class to find out favorite food commercials. Graph the results. Discuss what makes the most common ones so appealing.

Answers

Teacher check

Food Commercials

1. View TV food commercials. Record the information about four products in the table below.

Food product	Attention-grabbing messages	Selling Appeal												
		save money	convenient	makes us happy	healthier	tastes good	we'll look better	saves time	easy to use	celebrities	fun	lively music	trendy people	good food pictures
(a)														
(b)														
(c)														
(d)														

2. Which product would you choose to buy?

Explain. _____

_____

3. What makes an advertisement appealing to you?

_____

_____

4. Is your favorite TV commercial for ...

☐ fast food?

☐ healthy food? or

☐ junk food?

HEALTH CHALLENGE

If food commercials make you feel hungry, grab an apple or a piece of your favorite fruit.

WHAT IS EXERCISE?

Indicators

- Reads information that defines exercise.
- Comprehends information that defines exercise.

Teacher information

- The US Department of Health and Human Services recommends that children participate in at least 30 minutes of enjoyable, moderate-intensity activity every day and at least 30 minutes of vigorous physical exercise at least 3 or 4 days per week. Children who do little or no exercise should be encouraged to do at least 30 minutes a day to begin with. Health experts suggest that adults should do 30 minutes of exercise (which can be moderate) at least five days a week.

- Exercise can work on aerobic and anaerobic power, muscular strength and flexibility. Aerobic activity is exercise such as running or swimming, in which the heartbeat increases above its usual rate for an extended period of time. Anaerobic activity is exercise done in quick, short bursts, such as weight-lifting or sprinting.

- Read the information text with the students. Ask them to suggest other sports or physical activities they know that fit into one or more of these categories. The students can then complete the questions independently. Some of the answers to Question 3 could be shared with the class.

Additional activities

- In a small group, create posters to display around the school that explain what exercise is and what it can do for us.

- Choose a sport and use resources like the Internet to write a profile about it. Include information about its health benefits.

Answers

1. Teacher check
2. (a) false
   (b) true
   (c) false
3. Answers will vary

What Is Exercise?

To exercise is to do some kind of physical activity. The word "exercise" can mean different things to different people—from playing hockey to working out in the gym or playing golf.

Most health experts recommend that children do between 30 and 60 minutes of exercise each day to keep their bodies healthy. The time we spend exercising should include a variety of physical activities.

Exercise can:
- Strengthen your heart (e.g., running, swimming, or football).
- Build up muscle (e.g., weight-lifting, rowing, or cycling).
- Increase your flexibility (e.g., dancing, yoga, or gymnastics).

Some types of exercise can help to do more than one of these things for your body.

Answer these questions.

1. Write three sports or types of exercise that fit into each category. You can use examples from the text or your own ideas.

	Sport or exercise
flexibility	
heart	
muscle	

2. True or false?

   (a) Most health experts say that you should do five minutes of exercise a day. | TRUE | FALSE |

   (b) Playing golf is a type of exercise. | TRUE | FALSE |

   (c) "Exercise" means to do some kind of mental activity. | TRUE | FALSE |

3. Which of the types of exercise from the text would you most like to do? Why?

_____

_____

_____

HEALTH CHALLENGE

Choose an activity which covers the three major aspects of exercising. Do it three times a week.

HEALTHY CHOICES

LUNAR FITNESS CENTER

Indicators

- Shows an understanding of different types of exercise.
- Completes a bird's-eye view of a fitness center.
- Designs a newspaper advertisement for a fitness center.

Teacher information

- Students will require scrap paper to complete Questions 1 and 2. Teachers may also like to bring in some sample advertising material for fitness centers to help the students complete Question 2.

- Read the information at the top of the page. Ask the students to suggest some ideas for what they could include in their fitness centers. Teachers may also like to sketch an example of a fitness center floor plan on the board. Ensure that students understand what is meant by a "bird's-eye view" before they begin working on their own designs.

- Read Question 2 with the students and discuss what information an advertisement for a fitness center might contain. The students can then complete the question independently.

Additional activities

- Organize a class visit to a community fitness or recreation center. Have the students complete a profile that details what the center offers.

- Ask the students to survey adults about their feelings towards fitness centers or health clubs. Compile the results and discuss the most common likes and dislikes.

Answers

Answers will vary

EXERCISE AND FITNESS

Lunar Fitness Center

Imagine it is the future. You have been asked to design a fitness center for the large number of people who now live on the moon. Because nobody can go outside to exercise, the center needs to offer a wide variety of types of exercise. This means:

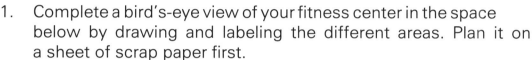

- *Areas with muscle-building equipment; e.g., a fitness circuit, a gym.*

- *Areas for classes or coaching in exercise that increases flexibility and/or heart rate; e.g., yoga rooms, basketball courts.*

You can also add anything else you think a good lunar fitness center should have!

1. Complete a bird's-eye view of your fitness center in the space below by drawing and labeling the different areas. Plan it on a sheet of scrap paper first.

entrance

changing rooms

2. Write a newspaper advertisement that tells people living on the moon what your fitness center offers; e.g., types of classes, equipment. Plan it on scrap paper first.

HEALTH CHALLENGE

Try exercising with a friend or a family member to stop yourself from getting bored and to keep you motivated.

BENEFITS OF EXERCISE

Indicators

- Reads information about the benefits of exercise.
- Answers questions about the benefits of exercise.

Teacher information

- Doing regular exercise has many health benefits. Fit people have less risk of stroke, some types of cancer and heart disease. They are also likely to maintain a healthy weight, live longer, and have lower blood pressure and cholesterol levels. In addition, exercise can make us feel good about ourselves by helping us to sleep better, feel more relaxed, and by improving our body image and self-esteem. This is particularly important in growing children and teenagers.

- Children who are physically active are far more likely to exercise regularly when they reach adulthood.

- Read the information text with the students. They can then complete the questions independently. They will require a dictionary to complete Question 1.

Additional activities

- Create flow charts to show what happens to the body when we exercise; e.g., heart rate increases, we begin to perspire.

- Draw labeled human body diagrams to show how exercise helps us on the inside and the outside.

- Research to find out more information about endorphins. Write the information as a report.

Answers

1. (a) something that happens at fixed times

   (b) feeling sure of yourself

   (c) something made by or used in chemical processes

2. Answers will vary

3. Answers will vary

Benefits of Exercise

Did you know?

- *Regular exercise helps to lessen the risk of heart disease, some forms of cancer and stroke. Weight-bearing exercise, like brisk walking or jogging, can also help to keep your bones strong.*

- *Playing a regular sport can improve your teamwork skills, make you feel more confident and help you to make new friends— among many other things!*

- *Exercise is important for the healthy development of children's bones and muscles.*

- *It is easier to keep your body at a healthy weight when you do regular exercise. This is because physical activity burns up fat. It also builds up muscle.*

- *When you exercise, your body releases chemicals called "endorphins." Endorphins help to make you feel happy. Exercise can also help you to sleep better, feel more relaxed about doing difficult things and give you loads more energy. This can make your self-esteem soar!*

Answer these questions.

1. Write dictionary meanings for these words.

    (a) regular _____

    (b) confident _____

    (c) chemicals _____

2. List the three benefits of exercise you think are the most important.

a	b	c

3. Why do you think playing sports regularly might make you feel more confident?

    _____

    _____

    _____

HEALTH CHALLENGE

With a group of friends, learn some physical skills together that you can show to your family or classmates at school; e.g., juggling, bouncing a soccer ball on your knees.

EXERCISE COMMERCIAL

Indicators

- Plans a television commercial that promotes exercise.
- Performs a television commercial in a small group that promotes exercise.

Teacher information

- Teachers may like to show some television "infomercials" to the students before they begin work on their own. Class notes could be made on the different features of each infomercial.

- Read the information at the top of the page and then allow the students to complete Questions 1 and 2 independently. Alternatively, teachers could allow pairs of students to work on these questions. When the questions are complete, the students should form groups of four or five. Teachers should guide the group discussions to help them to consider which commercials would be the easiest to perform with a small number of people. The students should then be allowed time to practice performing their chosen commercials. The amount of time given will depend on how long the teacher wants the commercials to be, whether costumes are used, etc. Encourage the students to use clear and strong voices when they are practicing.

- If a digital or video camera is available, the students' commercials could be taped and then shown to the class. If this is not possible, the commercials can be performed "live."

Additional activities

- In small groups, create a television segment about exercise that is suitable for young children to watch.

- Write catchy slogans on pieces of posterboard that encourage people to exercise. Display the slogans around the school.

- Working in a small group research campaigns like "Jump rope for heart" and plan a similar exercise-orientated campaign.

Answers

Answers will vary

Exercise Commercial

Design a television "infomercial" (a commercial that gives information) to encourage children of your age to exercise regularly.

1. Write notes about how you want your commercial to look and sound.

   • What information will your commercial give?

   • What kind of music or sound effects will you use?

   • What images will your commercial show? (e.g., people, settings and objects)

2. Describe what will happen in your commercial from beginning to end.

   Beginning: _____

   _____

   Middle: _____

   _____

   _____

   End: _____

   _____

3. Form a small group with other students. Everyone should read their commercial idea aloud.

4. Choose an idea that everyone likes and try acting it out. You may need to make a few changes so that it can be performed by the number of people in your group.

5. After you have practiced, either perform your commercial for the class, or film it and have the class watch it on television.

HEALTH CHALLENGE

Write a list of fun, active things you can do when you next think "I'm bored!"; e.g., backyard ballgame, using a jumping rope, going for a scavenger hunt. Check off your ideas as you try them.

DAILY FITNESS

Indicators

- Reads information about fitting exercise into our daily lives.

- Answers questions about fitting exercise into our daily lives.

Teacher information

- Some ways that teachers and parents can encourage children to exercise include:
  - Introducing fun physical activities like games and dancing.
  - Helping children to find a type of exercise they really enjoy by allowing them to try a variety of different sports or other physical activities.
  - Participating in physical activities with their students or children.
  - Limiting time spent playing computer games and watching television.
  - Planning outings that involve physical activity.

- Have the students read the information text and then volunteer other ways they could fit exercise into their daily lives. The questions can then be completed independently. Students may require a dictionary or thesaurus to complete Question 2.

Additional activities

- Write a creative narrative about a fictional character who loves doing exercise. What happens to him/her? (Note: Be careful not to promote overexercising).

- Create lists of fun ways that teachers could fit exercise into a school day to display in the staff room.

- Ask pairs of students to create role-plays based on their answers to Question 1.

Answers

1. Answers will vary

2. (a) energetic, robust, etc.

   (b) Answers will vary

3. Answers will vary, but might include the following:

   struggle, type, fit, daily, throwing, dance

Daily Fitness

Everyone is different when it comes to exercise. Some people find it easy to make time for exercise they enjoy. Others struggle to find a type of exercise they like and that fits into their lives.

The good news is that it is never too late to start doing exercise. If you don't do any exercise, or do very little, you should start by doing 20 minutes three times a week and then try to increase this to 30 to 60 minutes a day.

You can fit exercise into your daily life by doing things like walking instead of getting a ride in the car, playing on playground equipment, throwing a Frisbee® with your brother or sister, or going to a dance class. Once you have started, you should gradually build up to doing a mix of moderate exercise (e.g., walking) and vigorous exercise (e.g., playing a team sport).

What other ways of exercising could you fit into your life?

Answer these questions.

1. Write what you could say to someone your age who says "I can't find time to do any exercise."

2. (a) Write a synonym for the word "vigorous."

   _____

   (b) Give three examples of vigorous exercise.

3. Complete this paragraph with words that make sense.

   Some people _____ to find a _____ of exercise that

   they can _____ into their lives. But we can all fit exercise into our

   _____ lives by doing things like _____ a Frisbee® or

   going to a _____ class.

   ### HEALTH CHALLENGE

   If you have to do household chores like washing the car or dusting, make them fun by doing them in time to your favorite music.

HEALTHY CHOICES

DAILY FITNESS SCHEDULE

Indicator

• Plans his/her own daily fitness schedule to suit a school day.

Teacher information

• Read and discuss the information at the top of the page with the students. Ensure they understand the difference between vigorous and moderate exercise. Supply them with scrap paper to write ideas before they complete the schedule on the page. They can then complete the questions independently. The students could compare their answers in small groups.

Additional activities

• Have the students list all the physical activities they do over a weekend day and compare it to their schoolday schedules.

• Compile a list of the most popular physical activities students indicated they would like to try. Experts on these activities could be invited to speak to the class.

Answers

Answers will vary

EXERCISE AND FITNESS

Daily Fitness Schedule

Write a fitness schedule for a schoolday in your life. You need to show how you could fit in at least 30 minutes of exercise.

You can include activities you already do now and add some new activities you would like to try. Include a mix of moderate and more vigorous exercise. You may need to write some ideas on scrap paper first.

Before-school fitness activity	Time spent (minutes)

During-school fitness activity	Time spent (minutes)

After-school fitness activity	Time spent (minutes)

- How many minutes of fitness did you end up with for the whole day?

- Did you find it difficult to make up at least 30 minutes of fitness?

YES   NO

- Would you describe most of your activities as moderate or vigorous?

_____

- Were any of the activities you wrote new for you? If so, circle them.

HEALTH CHALLENGE

For a different physical activity, try making kites with your family and then testing them out in a local park.

TRAINING SCHEDULES

Indicators

- Reads information about the training schedules of elite athletes.
- Answers questions about the training schedules of elite athletes.

Teacher information

- Allow the students to read the information text and then discuss their feelings and opinions about what they have read. The students can then complete the questions. Answers to Question 4 could be shared with the class.

Additional activities

- Invite a professional athlete or Olympic-level athlete to speak to the class about his/her training schedule.
- Find out the amounts and types of foods an athlete eats while in training. How does it compare to students' diets?
- Find out what effects overexercising has on the body.

Answers

1. Answers will vary but should indicate that a rower would do this to build up muscle to be able to row more quickly.

2. five to six

3. Answers should include running drills, swimming, weight training, cycling, or skills sessions.

4. Answers will vary

Training Schedules

What kind of exercise program does a top athlete have to maintain? Olympic-level professional athletes would spend five to six days a week in training. This would include lots of different types of exercise. For example, an Olympic rower would not only row, but would also do weight training and maybe play a team sport like soccer. An NFL player's training sessions could include running drills, swimming, weight training, cycling and skills sessions.

Here is an example of a training schedule for a high achieving disabled US athlete.

Sarah Will

Sarah Will was paralyzed from the waist down due to a skiing accident.
She learned to use a monoski and became a member of the US Disabled Ski Team. She is a national champion, has won 2 gold medals at the Paralympics and was the world champion in disabled skiing. Sarah trains by pushing her road racer at least 12 miles a day and lifting weights. She waterskis and competes in 10 km road races across the US. During her winter training (November to April), Sarah skis 5 to 6 days a week.

Answer these questions.

1. Why do you think a rower might do weight training? _____

    _____

2. How many days a week would you expect an Olympic athlete to train for?

    _____

3. Write two things an NFL player's training session might include.

    _____   _____

4. How do you think you would cope with Sarah Will's training schedule?

not well	okay
very well	easily

    Give a reason for your answer.

    _____

    _____

    _____

    _____

    _____

    _____

    _____

HEALTH CHALLENGE

Try a style of dancing that appeals to you —it burns up lots of energy and is fun too!

HEALTHY CHOICES

ATHLETE PROFILE

Indicators

- Uses information resources to research an athlete.
- Completes a profile of an athlete.

Teacher information

- See "Teacher information" on page 54 for suggestions on finding resources on athletes.
- Students will need access to the Internet or other resources to complete their research. The research could be completed by individual students or pairs of students. The profiles should be shared with the class and compared.

Additional activities

- Write a diary entry for a training day in the life of the athlete students chose to profile and express their feelings about his/her training.
- Students write a fan letter to their favorite athlete, saying why they admire him/her. Email or mail it to him/her.

Answers

Answers will vary

Athlete Profile

1. Use the Internet or other resources to research an Olympic-level or professional athlete you admire. Complete the following profile.

- Name of person _____
- Age _____
- Nationality _____
- Sport _____
- Greatest sporting achievements _____

2. Write three facts about how this person trains for his/her sport.

a
b
c

3. Write how you think this person would answer the following question.

"Do you think that all the training you do is worth it? Why/Why not?"

_____
_____
_____
_____
_____

HEALTH CHALLENGE

Think about what you have to do to achieve a personal fitness goal.

COMMUNITY FITNESS

Indicators

- Reads information about the fitness opportunities offered by a local community.
- Answers questions about the fitness opportunities offered by a local community.

Teacher information

- Allow the students to read the information text. Teachers can then lead a class discussion in which the students discuss what fitness opportunities are offered by their local communities. The students can then complete the questions.

Additional activities

- Prepare and deliver a speech as the Mayor of Bridlevale, discussing ideas for the new fitness facility he/she wants built. Give reasons why it should be built.
- Design the perfect children's park. It should appeal to all ages and offer opportunities for physical activity. Think about playground equipment, picnic areas, volleyball courts, entertainment, etc.

Answers

1. Answers will vary but should include two of the following: cycling, hiking, tennis, basketball, aerobics, dancing, skateboarding, rollerblading, swimming, kayaking, or horseback riding.
2. The symbols should indicate a fully-equipped gym, tennis, basketball, aerobics and dancing classes.
3. Answers will vary

EXERCISE AND FITNESS

Community Fitness

Local communities and councils do many things to encourage people to keep fit. Read about the facilities, events and programs available in the town of Bridlevale.

Keeping Fit in Bridlevale

Bridlevale offers:

- Six parks with playground equipment, walking trails and some fitness circuit equipment; e.g., chin-up bars

- Cycling tours by Mountain View River

- Free weekly guided hiking trips in the Newington Hills

- A community fitness center with a fully-equipped gym, tennis courts and a basketball court

- Low-cost aerobics and dance classes at the community fitness center

- A skateboard and rollerblading park

- An 18-hole golf course

- An Olympic-sized swimming pool

- Regular community fitness days with expert instructors teaching people "adventure" sports like kayaking, and horseback riding

Answer these questions.

1. Name two sports people living in Bridlevale could "enjoy" or "try."

   _____   _____

2. Draw symbols to show what is available at Bridlevale's community fitness center. For example, a symbol for football might look like this:

3. Imagine you are the Mayor of Bridlevale. You decide to build another fitness facility. What would you suggest and why?

   _____

   _____

   _____

   _____

   _____

HEALTH CHALLENGE

With a family member or a friend, try out a fitness facility or program offered by your community that is new to both of you.

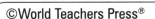

HOW FIT IS YOUR COMMUNITY?

Exercise and Fitness

Indicators

- Interprets symbols on simple maps.
- Reads and comprehends resource material about his/her local community.

Teacher information

- Students will require a street directory or a map of their local area, resource material about the fitness events or programs offered by their community, and/or access to the Internet.
- If a street directory is used, teachers may need to guide students to locate their community's boundaries. They may also need to show the students the key to the symbols used in the directory (usually found in the first few pages of the directory).
- Students should complete the questions with a partner or small group. The answers to Question 4 can then be shared and discussed with the class.

Additional activities

- Hold a simple debate on the topic "Our community cares about the fitness of its people."
- Draw a map of a fictional community that actively promotes fitness. Use your own symbols to show the facilities available.
- Write a program for a community fitness day that appeals to both adults and children.

Answers

Answers will vary

How Fit Is Your Community?

Find out what facilities, events, or programs your community offers. Use the following:

- *A street directory page or map that shows the facilities and features of your area.*
- *Brochures or calendars produced by your local council or community groups.*
- *The Internet.*

1. Use the street directory or map to check off or write the fitness facilities found in your community.

   ☐ parks/reserves   ☐ cycling tracks   ☐ public swimming pools

   ☐ walking trails   ☐ golf courses   ☐ sports clubs

   ☐ playgrounds

   Other: _____

   _____

2. Use the brochures, calendars, or the Internet to give examples of the types of fitness events or programs that are offered.

   _____

   _____

   _____

   _____

3. Rate the variety of fitness facilities, events and programs in your area.

   | excellent |
   | good |
   | okay |
   | needs improving |

4. What changes to the fitness facilities, events, or programs would you like to see?

   _____

   _____

   _____

   _____

   _____

   HEALTH CHALLENGE

   Explore parks, nature reserves, or waterways within easy driving distance of your home.

HEALTHY CHOICES

A BALANCED LIFESTYLE

Indicators

- Reads information about a balanced lifestyle.
- Answers questions about a balanced lifestyle.

Teacher information

- We enjoy a variety of foods from many different countries. The key to good health is eating a variety of foods from all food groups in moderation. Getting regular exercise, adequate sleep, and balancing the demands of work and school with relaxation help to provide a balanced, healthy lifestyle. More emphasis on one area while neglecting another causes stress, poor health, and the inability to cope with the demands of daily life.

- Students should read the text and highlight any important information. The meanings of unknown words may be found in a dictionary or discussed as a class.

- Students read and answer the questions.

Additional activities

- Students create posters encouraging a more balanced approach to life.

- As a class, consider the disadvantages of putting more emphasis on one area of life than on other areas. Discuss this in relation to the lives of elite athletes, such as Olympians, or businesspeople who work more than twelve hours each day or six or seven days a week.

- Students create a pie graph which shows the different aspects of their lives in relation to each other.

Answers

1. Teacher check
2. eating/diet, physical activity, work, relaxation and sleep
3. Teacher check
4. Sedentary activities are those which require sitting or little movement.
5. Teacher check
6. 10 or 11 hours

SELF-MANAGEMENT

64

A Balanced Lifestyle

1. Read the information below and highlight important points.

Most experts agree that to achieve a healthy lifestyle we should establish a balance between eating and physical activity, work, relaxation and sleep.

- *Eating a balanced diet involves eating the right amount of food from each of the basic food groups, as well as enjoying treats occasionally. Drinking water every day helps to replace water lost from the body. Soft drinks should be considered occasional treats.*

- *Sedentary activities such as computer games, Internet use, television and homework should be balanced with active pursuits such as sports, bike riding, taking the dog for a walk, or playing games outside with friends. Not more than two hours each day should be spent on sedentary pursuits, if possible.*

- *School plays an important part in the lives of children, but time also should be allowed for relaxation or pursuing hobbies or interests.*

- *Our bodies need time to recover from mental and physical activities, so getting a reasonable number of hours sleep of each night is recommended. Most children between the ages of 5 and 12 average about 9.5 hours sleep each night, but many health experts think that 10 or 11 each night may be better.*

2. What are the main areas which need to be kept in balance to have a healthy lifestyle?

3. List some foods which should be only eaten occasionally.

4. Explain what is meant by "sedentary" activities.

5. List some interests or hobbies which help you to relax.

6. How many hours of sleep should a child your age have each night?

HEALTH CHALLENGE

Select one area of your diet which may need changing. Try to carry out the change for a week!

HEALTHY CHOICES
65

FINDING THE BALANCE

Indicators

- Identifies areas of his/her life which need improvement.
- Suggests ways to implement life changes.

Teacher information

- Students should check those sentences which best describe areas of their life relating to diet, exercise, schoolwork, relaxation and sleep. Students should select those sentences checked which indicate they need to improve some areas of their life. For example, if the student has checked any of the sentences (b), (d), (e) and (g), this indicates that there are areas of their lives which may need to be changed.
- Students should write suggestions for changes to complete Question 2.

Additional activities

- Students form five groups—one for each area (diet, exercise, sleep, relaxation, schoolwork). Brainstorm to find ways to make improvements and list these on a chart. Students can rotate around each group until all class members have put suggestions on each of the five charts. These can be displayed in the room for students to refer to when ideas are needed.
- Students keep a record of changes made and record how they feel at the end of a given period after implementing them.
- Students collect magazine and newspaper articles about personalities who they believe have balance in their lives. Students write a report about one of these people and explain why he/she has a balanced life.

Answers

Answers will vary

SELF-MANAGEMENT

Finding the Balance

A person who has a balanced life tries to eat healthy food, gets regular exercise, enjoys some relaxation as well as work, and gets enough sleep to cope with the physical demands of daily life.

1. Check the sentences which best describe aspects of your life.

    (a)   My diet is reasonably healthy.

    (b)   My diet needs improvement.

    (c)   I get enough exercise each week.

    (d)   I need to exercise more each week.

    (e)   I spend a lot of time doing things that are not very active.

    (f)   I spend two hours or less on sedentary activities.

    (g)   I spend too much time on schoolwork each day.

    (h)   I have interests which help me to relax.

    (i)   I get enough sleep every night.

2. Using the sentences above to refer to, write some ways in which you can improve areas of your life to provide more balance.

diet		exercise
	sleep	
relaxation		school-work

HEALTH CHALLENGE

Choose a suggestion from one of the areas to try for a week. Decide whether you felt better or not and why.

HEALTHY CHOICES

STRESS LESS!

Indicators

- Reads information about stress.
- Completes sentences about stress.

Teacher information

- The process of growing up can be stressful for children. The pace of life is faster, changes occur rapidly and children are expected to perform better at school and cope with all other aspects of life, often without having any idea of strategies to deal with stress. Situations beyond the control of children will cause them stress. These include death, divorce, family health problems, parental and school demands, peer pressure, media influences and others. Stress can affect the emotional, social and academic areas of a child's life.

- Children who suffer from stress may display the following signs or symptoms:
    - Headaches, stomachaches, or neck pain
    - Irritability, sadness, panic, anger
    - Being more quiet than usual
    - Sleep or relaxation problems
    - Lethargy, daydreaming, withdrawal from activities
    - Excessive energy or restlessness
    - Nervous habits such as nail biting or hair chewing
    - Frowning, looking strained
    - Having trouble getting along with friends

- Children can learn to identify feelings of stress by changes in themselves such as rapid heartbeat, sweaty palms, fast breathing, stomachaches, tight, tense muscles and nervous, panicky feelings.

- Some ways to help children with stress include:
    - Physical contact such as hugging
    - Listening to expressions of feelings
    - Encouragement; i.e., giving praise
    - Honesty and openness—encouraging children to express their feelings openly
    - Security—being consistent
    - Physical exercise—provides an outlet to express stressful feelings
    - Humor—joking and laughing helps children to let out stressful feelings and to see the funny side of things
    - Quietness—providing times for quiet reflection and relaxation
    - Balanced diet—encouraging children to eat a healthy diet helps them to feel better inside and outside

- Students read the information and complete the questions independently.

Additional activities

- Survey students to tally and graph strategies that they use to cope with stress.
- As a class, brainstorm to list different strategies for coping with stress (whether they have been used or not). Students select one strategy to use over a weekly period and report about its effectiveness and the situations in which it is best applied.
- Students create posters in cool, calm colors which encourage others to STRESS LESS.

Answers

1. Teacher check
2. the practice of making assaults or attacks; offensive actions
3. (a) children
   (b) the demands placed on children by family, school, friends and self
   (c) Students should choose two of the following: talking to another person, relaxing, doing physical exercise, physical contact, such as hugs and kisses, humor such as joking and laughing, eating a balanced diet
   (d) overeat, lose their temper, or be aggressive.

SELF-MANAGEMENT

Stress Less!

Stress is a natural part of life. Children experience stress in their lives just as much as adults. Stress may be caused by many reasons. Demands of family, friends, school and self may cause stress. Stress can make it difficult to cope with daily problems as they occur.

There are ways of dealing with stress. These include:

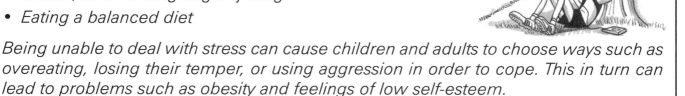

- *Talking to other people*
- *Relaxing by listening to music or finding a quiet place to go*
- *Doing physical exercise*
- *Physical contact, such as hugs from parents, grandparents*
- *Humor, such as laughing or joking*
- *Eating a balanced diet*

Being unable to deal with stress can cause children and adults to choose ways such as overeating, losing their temper, or using aggression in order to cope. This in turn can lead to problems such as obesity and feelings of low self-esteem.

Answer these questions.

1. Explain what it means by "Demands of family, friends, school and self ...."

   _____

   _____

2. Write a meaning for the word "aggression."

3. Complete the sentences with the correct word or words.

   (a) Adults and _____ experience stress in their lives.

   (b) Stress can be caused by:

   (c) Two ways of dealing with stress are:

   (d) A person who is unable to cope with stress may:

HEALTH CHALLENGE

When you are feeling stressed, try one of the ways above and see if it works! You may also like to try taking ten deep breaths!

STRATEGIES FOR COPING WITH STRESS

Indicators

- Identifies positive strategies for dealing with stress.
- Relates a stressful situation and tells what strategies were used to cope with it.

Teacher information

- Many students may not be aware they actually use strategies for dealing with stress, and some may be introduced to new ways of dealing with stressful situations.
- Allow the students to read the information at the top of the page.
- The students read the strategies listed in Question 1 and check those which they think are positive ways of dealing with stress. Discussion may be needed if students have different views about some strategies.
- Students underline those strategies listed that they may have used then write about a stressful situation which they may encounter and how they might cope with the stress. They can then discuss it with a friend to compare ways different people might deal with the same situation.

NOTE: Some students may not feel comfortable talking about situations which are stressful, such as bullying or having to cope with a new stepparent. Sensitivity should be shown to these students and their problems.

Additional activities

- Organize two charts and label one "Positive strategies for dealing with stress" and the other "Negative strategies for dealing with stress." When students have some free time, they can add suggestions to the chart. Encourage students to add more fun activities such as "climb a mountain," "role-play being a teenage pop idol and lip-sync a favorite song," "make a monstrous sandcastle on the beach and jump on it" to show that life can be fun and not everything has to be serious all the time.
- Spend a short time after breaks carrying out "stress-relieving activities" such as stretching, quiet reading, singing, or dancing to a popular tune. To relieve stress, relaxing music may be played while the students work.
- Role-play various stressful situations and show ways of dealing with them with a minimum of stress.

Answers

Teacher check

SELF-MANAGEMENT

Strategies for Coping with Stress

We all have to deal with stress at some stage of our lives. Finding positive ways to do this can be a challenge at times. It is easy to make ourselves feel better by eating a chocolate cake, throwing a temper tantrum, or sulking. In the long run, these types of strategies are not helpful and may lead to problems such as eating disorders and not being able to get along with others.

Answer these questions.

1. Read the strategies below and check those which you think are good ways of dealing with stress.

    (a)   eating chocolate and other candy

    (b)   reading a book

    (c)   listening to music

    (d)   sulking

    (e)   hitting or punching another person

    (f)   talking to a friend, teacher, or parent

    (g)   going for a walk or jog

    (h)   saying nasty things to friends or parents

    (i)   having a laugh about whatever is wrong

    (j)   biting fingernails or chewing hair

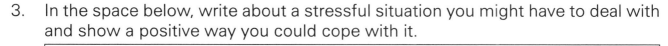

2. Underline the ways you have used yourself.

3. In the space below, write about a stressful situation you might have to deal with and show a positive way you could cope with it.

4. Discuss the situation with a friend to see what he/she would do.

HEALTH CHALLENGE

Select one of the good ways to deal with stress and try it out to see if it works.

BODY IMAGE

Indicators

- Learns about body image.
- Identifies factors which affect body image.

Teacher information

- An unrealistic body image can lead to self-destructive behavior such as dieting or binge eating. Many people diet at least once in their lives. Embarrassment about appearance can cause people to stop exercising because they do not want people to see their bodies. This, in turn, can further contribute to a more sedentary lifestyle with increased risk of obesity, diabetes and heart disease.

- Children are influenced by parental attitudes. If a parent puts a lot of emphasis on appearance and dieting, then so will the child.

- An individual's identity is not determined solely by his/her appearance but also upon aspects such as personality, skills, talents and attitude to life. Emphasis should be given to these aspects of each individual to develop positive self-esteem.

- Students will need a dictionary to write the meanings of the words from the passage.

- Students should read the text through once before completing the cloze passage, using the words in bold print.

- Students form small groups to discuss reasons why people may have a poor body image. These can be listed and reported back to the class.

Additional activities

- Students cut pictures from magazines of people they admire and create a collage. (Encourage students to include lots of people with skills, talents and motivation.)

- Students create colorful posters of qualities which they admire in people. These may include words such as "determination," "motivation," "drive," "dedication," "kind," "caring," "consideration," "well-mannered."

- Students read stories or view biographies about people who have achieved great things (even though they may not be particularly attractive in a physical sense).

Answers

1. (a) a likeness of a person, animal or thing; form; appearance

   (b) a lack of order or regular arrangement; confusion

   (c) low in spirits; dejected; feeling unhappy

   (d) favorable opinion of oneself

2. Teacher check

3. Teacher check

SELF-MANAGEMENT

Body Image

Body image is how you **think** *and* **feel** *about your body and what you* **imagine** *it looks like. It may have nothing at all to do with how you* **actually** *look! A lot of people are not* **happy** *with the way they look. This can cause them to develop eating* **disorders**, *become* **depressed** *or anxious, and have low* **self-esteem***; i.e., they don't think they are worthwhile people.*

We are all different in **appearance** *and the way we* **think** *and* **act***. Our bodies are all* **different** *shapes and sizes. We need to make the* **best** *of ourselves just as we are!*

Nobody *is perfect and* **no body** *is perfect!*

1. Use your dictionary to find the meaning of the following words.

(a) image
(b) disorder
(c) depressed
(d) self-esteem

2. Complete the cloze, using the words in bold print above.

   Body image is how you _____ and _____ about

   your body and what you _____ it looks like. It may have nothing

   at all to do with how you _____ look! A lot of people are not

   _____ with the way they look. This can cause them to develop

   eating _____, become _____ or anxious, and have

   low _____.

   We are all different in _____ and the way we _____

   or _____. Our bodies are all _____ shapes and

   sizes. We need to make the _____ of ourselves as we are!

   _____ is perfect and _____ is perfect!

3. Write about or discuss things which may influence a person's image of himself/herself.

> **HEALTH CHALLENGE**
>
> *Write a list of all the things you like about yourself. You are not allowed to include anything that you DON'T like!*

BODY IMAGE, THE MEDIA AND OTHER PEOPLE

Indicator

- Completes information about body image.

Teacher information

- We are constantly bombarded with images in the media about how we should look. If we don't look like the images on television or in magazines, then we may start to feel that we are not as good as everyone else. Very few people have flawless features and perfect bodies. This inability to meet the standards set by others may lead to low self-esteem.

- Other people we come into contact with may also influence our opinion of ourselves with positive and negative comments.

- Some strategies which help with positive body image include:
  - Think positively—focus on the things that you like about yourself.
  - Associate with people who have a healthy attitude towards food, weight and body image.
  - Eat healthy food. Aim to be as healthy as possible and you will look better on the outside as well as feel better on the inside.
  - Be as active as you can. Find some exercise which you enjoy doing and start doing it. Exercising makes you feel better about your body, helps you to relax or relieve stress, and gives you more energy.

- Students read the text and answer the questions.

Note: Shy students or those with a poor body image may not wish to share their answers to questions on this worksheet with others. Consideration for their feelings should be shown.

Additional activities

- Students choose and research the biography of a well-known personality who does not fit the "usual mold"; i.e., tall, dark and handsome, or slim, tanned and blonde.

- Discuss the health risks of getting skin cancer in the quest for a tanned body.

- Each student writes his/her name on a sheet of art paper. The paper is passed to a number of students with each student writing one nice comment about that person.

- The teacher creates an "imaginary" student with some things they do not like about themselves. The class offers positive suggestions to improve these, where possible.

Answers

1–2. Teacher check

3. Answers will vary

Body Image, the Media and Other People

Images of people on television and in magazines emphasize beauty and thinness. This makes us think that we need to look the same.

We need to be careful about this and learn to appreciate ourselves just as we are. This does not mean that we can't make the best of what we have!

1. Write a list of five things you like about your body. For example, "I have beautiful big eyes," or "I have nice hands."

Did you know that how you feel on the inside affects what you look like on the outside? Feeling good about yourself is called having good self-esteem.

2. Write four good things to say to yourself each morning to improve your self-esteem. This may include aspects other than things about your body, for example, "I am a good friend," "I am helpful to other people," "People like my drawings so I must be a good artist."

    1.
    2.
    3.
    4.

We are often influenced by what our friends think and do. We like to be part of a group and be liked by them. Sometimes this can be bad because we are all different and can't be the same!

3. Give three reasons why it is good to be yourself.

    *   _____
    *   _____
    *   _____

HEALTH CHALLENGE

Each day find one nice thing to say to a different student in your class, but try to really mean it!

MAKING CHOICES

Indicators

• Reads information about making choices.

• Shows understanding of the influences on individual choices.

Teacher information

• The decisions for young children are most often made by their parents. As children get older, they begin to make more choices for themselves to assert their independence. They also need to take responsibility for the decisions they make, whether they have positive or negative consequences. Some decisions are easy and have little consequence, such as choosing what to eat for breakfast. Others are more difficult, and decisions regarding these need to be planned.

• A simple plan when making decisions follows the steps below:

  – Decide what the problem is.

  – Decide what the choices are.

  – Think of all the consequences of the choices.

  – Select the best choice based on the information gained from the previous steps.

• Often children make decisions based on whether it will help them fit into their particular group or not. They may make decisions which they know are wrong in order to achieve this goal. Children need to develop enough confidence to say "no" if a decision is harmful to themselves or others.

• Students read and discuss the text, then answer the questions.

Additional activities

• As a class, discuss situations when peer pressure may be good and times when it may be bad.

• Students relate incidents when they have bought or asked parents to buy something which they have lost interest in very quickly. Why do they think this was?

• Students write a short text and plan a role-play to encourage people to buy a particular product. Students can perform these for the class.

Answers

1. Teacher check

2. Teacher check

3. Answers will vary

Making Choices

Every day we have to make many choices and decisions.

What will I have for breakfast? How much money do I need to take if I decide to buy my lunch? Which book will I borrow from the library? What games will I play at lunchtime? What television program will I watch after school?

We should make choices because they are the best ones for us, but often the decisions we make are influenced by our friends, family and the media.

Friends have a lot of influence over each other. Because we all like to feel that we belong to a group, we often act and do things because others in the group are doing them. Groups like to wear the same clothes and do the same things. Peer pressure can be good but sometimes it can be bad!

Advertisements can be very persuasive. They encourage us to buy their products, do the things they want us to do, and look the way they want us to look.

Answer these questions.

1. Explain how friends can influence choices that we make.

2. Explain how advertisements in magazines and on television influence our choices.

3. Write about the last time you chose to do something because a friend wanted you to do it.

HEALTH CHALLENGE

Be a critical viewer of advertisements! Think about whether the ad is truthful and what the advertisers are doing to make you want to buy the product. Do you really like the product, or do you want it because everyone else has one?

HEALTHIER CHOICES

Indicators

- Reads and answers questions about making healthier choices.
- Identifies healthier choices from a selection.

Teacher information

- Being fit and healthy often only requires a little effort each day. Most children are aware of the basic food groups at this age and are able to make simple decisions for a healthier lifestyle. Often students need to be presented with alternatives from which to choose. Many children may not know whether a healthier food choice is tasty or not if they have not been able to try it. As they get older, children can be more adventurous with their diet. As adults we need to encourage students to be "well-rounded" individuals and present them with opportunities to carry out both sedentary activities, such as reading and information technology, as well as active pursuits.

- The best way to encourage students to lead a healthier lifestyle is to set a good example!

- Students read the text and explain what it means in their own words to answer Question 1.

- Students underline the healthier alternative in each line in Question 2 and write how often to include the less active or less healthy pursuit.

- Question 3 asks students to find ways to add more incidental movement to their daily activities.

Additional activities

- Students participate in moving, stretching, or relaxation activities after activities in the classroom which require a lot of sitting.

- Bring a pedometer into the room to allow students to take turns to see how many steps are taken each day by different individuals. Discuss reasons why differences occur and ways to add more steps to each day. Students try to better the score of the last student. Ensure that students carry out normal school activities and are not disrupting other class members by walking around the classroom all day.

- Students contribute healthy recipes to a class cookbook for each student to take home.

Answers

1. Teacher check

2. The students should have selected the following alternatives:
   (a) banana (b) chicken nuggets and salad (c) watermelon (d) yogurt (e) oven-baked chicken (f) play football (g) build a model (h) play with the dog (i) walk to school (j) get up to change channels

3. Teacher check

Healthier Choices

As we become more independent, we make more choices for ourselves. We can choose to be more healthy and fit so that we do not get health problems later in life. We can make healthier food choices and still enjoy takeout food occasionally! We can choose to exercise regularly and still enjoy computer games as well!

The important thing is to have balance!

1. Explain in your own words how life can be "balanced."

   _____

   _____

   _____

2. Underline the healthier food and exercise choices in the list. In the box next to each group write how often to include the less healthy alternative.

   (a) banana   cookies   ☐

   (b) chicken nuggets and fries chicken nuggets and salad ☐

   (c) candy   watermelon   ☐

   (d) ice cream   yogurt   ☐

   (e) fried chicken   oven-baked chicken   ☐

   (f) watch a DVD   play football   ☐

   (g) use the computer   build a model   ☐

   (h) play with the dog   watch a television program ☐

   (i) walk to school   travel by car to school   ☐

   (j) use the remote control   get up to change channels ☐

3. Adding more incidental movement during the day can aid fitness. List some ways to be more active each day.

   ┌─────────────────────────────────┐
   │   │
   │   │
   │   │
   └─────────────────────────────────┘

HEALTH CHALLENGE

Devise your own special recipe for healthy homemade hamburgers to try at home! Ask Mom or Dad if you can try it at home for dinner one night! You can even help to cook it!

WHAT TYPE OF EXERCISE IS RIGHT FOR ME?

Indicators

- Reads information about factors which influence exercise choices.
- Completes a table to select a form of exercise suitable for himself/herself.

Teacher information

- Adults and children need to find a form of exercise which they will continue to do because they enjoy it. Exercise should use and develop physical talents and skills. It should be fun! Sometimes one form of exercise needs to be changed for another to prevent boredom but maintain physical activity.

- Economic and physical conditions need to be taken into consideration before deciding to take up particular forms of exercise. Activities which cost a lot of money to attend or require the purchase of lots of equipment, and activities which have facilities some distance away may not be good choices.

- Students read the information and answer the questions.

- Many students may already be participating in various activities which involve exercise. Completing Question 2 may give them a greater understanding of why they chose that particular form of exercise or may help them to choose a different one if they wish to change.

- Students should select the form of exercise which falls into most of the categories listed. If cost is not a problem, students may have more options to choose from.

Additional activities

- Brainstorm to list on a chart "fun" ways to exercise which do not cost anything; for example, throw a Frisbee® in the park, climb a hill, go for a bike ride, go blackberry picking with the family, have breakfast on the beach and collect shell specimens or build a huge sandcastle, or take the dog for a walk around the block.

- Students report on a new form of exercise they have started so other students are able to decide if they would like to try it too.

- Research for information about "extreme" sports and discuss the safety aspects.

Answers

Teacher check

What Type of Exercise Is Right for Me?

We are individuals with different likes and dislikes, opinions, skills and talents. The type of exercise which one person chooses can often be different from that of another person. If you haven't exercised very much before, how do you know where to start?

Many factors affect the type of exercise you do. These include:

- *Your interests, talents and skills*
- *What the form of exercise costs*
- *The availability of resources, equipment and facilities*
- *If it will be easy to fit into a regular weekly schedule*
- *If you will be able to have a friend to go with or if you will be happy to attend by yourself*
- *Transportation*

1. Complete the boxes with activities to show a form of exercise just right for you!

Exercise where your interests, talents or skills are used	Facilities or equipment available locally
Exercise which doesn't cost anything to participate in	Forms of exercise which you will be able to do regularly
Exercise you can do with a friend	Exercise where transportation is needed

HEALTH CHALLENGE

Choose a form of exercise you would like to try (e.g., kite flying) and research for information to show you how to start.

2. The best exercise for me is

_____

_____

_____

GOAL SETTING

Indicators

- Reads information about goal setting.
- Identifies goals and formulates plans to carry them out.

Teacher information

- People who set goals experience success. They formulate goals and use specific strategies to meet them. Goals need to be achievable and personally important. They need to be clearly defined and have a specific plan of action. Steps to achieving a goal include:
  - Expressing the goal in terms of specific events or behavior.
  - Expressing the goal in terms which can be achieved.
  - Setting a timeline for the goal.
  - Choosing a goal which can be controlled.
  - Planning and organizing a strategy that will help to reach the goal.
  - Defining the goal in terms of steps.
  - Being accountable for progress towards the goal.

- Students should select simple goals, such as trying to eat five servings of vegetables and two of fruit each day, drinking more water daily, or trying to include some exercise each day and reduce the amount of time spent on the computer or in front of the television.

- Students read the text. Select an example to complete with them to show the steps which may be taken. For example, for a goal which includes trying to include the right amount of fruit and vegetables each day, the steps may be set up as a daily menu or food diary. This may include fruit with cereal and milk for breakfast fruit with vegetable sticks for a morning snack with vegetable sticks, salad with cold meat in a sandwich with another piece of fruit for lunch and stir-fry vegetables with meat for dinner.

- Students may find it easier to write in a number of activities which lead to achieving their goal rather than steps which lead from one to the other.

Additional activities

- Students complete a food and exercise diary for a week. At the end of the week they evaluate whether they have achieved their goal or not.
- Students formulate goals for getting along with other students or parents, or for improving an academic subject or working habit.
- Students select a career they would like to have in the future and define the steps towards achieving it. Some research may be needed for this activity.

Answers

Teacher check

SELF-MANAGEMENT

Goal Setting

Setting goals helps you to achieve something which is important to you. A plan will help you to reach your goal. The plan should have steps.

In order to achieve a more balanced, healthy lifestyle, set goals for each of the headings below. Show the steps taken to achieve the goal and the time taken.

My plan for achieving a healthy diet goal

My goal is _____

The steps to reach my goal are _____

_____

_____

_____

_____

I will reach my goal on_____

My plan for achieving an exercise goal

My goal is _____

The steps to reach my goal are _____

_____

_____

_____

_____

I will reach my goal on_____

HEALTH CHALLENGE

Start a food and exercise diary to record what you are eating and how much exercise you are doing each day!

www.worldteacherspress.com

HEALTHY CHOICES